ST. LAWRENCE I.
Gambell

Nome

...bue

...Range

Bering Strait

Point Barrow   HERALD I.   WRANGEL I.

ARCTIC

DE LONG IS.   NEW SIBERIAN IS.

Cape Chelyuskin

NORTHERN LAND

Taimyr Peninsula

Lena

80   70

S.   S.   I.   A.   R.

WARD HUNT I.   T-3

Cape Nares   OCEAN
Cape Columbia
Cape Hecla
Cape Sheridan

Alert

Peary Land
Navy Cliff
Independence Fjord

RUDOLF I.

PRINCESS THYRA I.
PRINCESS MARGARETHE I.

WHITE I.   FRANZ JOSEF LAND

NOVAYA ZEMLYA

SPITZBERGEN

BARENTS   SEA

CLAVERING I.
NORWEGIAN

JAN MAYEN I.   Murmansk   Kola Peninsula

SEA

FAROE IS.

...AND

0

North

NORTH

THE NATURE AND DRAMA
OF THE POLAR WORLD

Kaare Rodahl, M.D.

HARPER & BROTHERS, PUBLISHERS

New York

Library of Congress catalog card number: 53-5381

To Joe Fletcher,
whose untiring efforts have blazed the trail for a new
approach to the exploration of the North Polar Basin.

Acknowledgments

The author is greatly indebted to Dr. H. U. Sverdrup, director of the Norwegian Polar Institute, Oslo, and Dr. E. F. DuBois, Professor Emeritus of Physiology, Cornell University Medical College, New York, for their valuable advice and criticism during the writing of this book. For the constructive help in the preparation of some of the chapters the author is indebted to Ambassador Dr. H. W:son Ahlmann, formerly head of the Geographical Institute, Stockholm Högskola. The valuable assistance of Mr. S. Richter, librarian of the Norwegian Polar Institute, and of Mrs. Siri Guldahl, is gratefully acknowledged.

For the constructive advice and criticism of Mrs. Marguerite Munson in the preparation of the manuscript, the author is also very grateful.

It is through the stimulating interest and the encouragement of Mr. Evan Thomas of Harper & Brothers that the task of writing this book has been undertaken.

K. R.

March, 1953

Contents

Illustrations

ix

Introduction

On March 19, 1952, a small group of men of the United States Air Force made the first successful landing on a floating island of ice, T-3, close to the North Pole. For thirteen days the three men who remained on the ice under the leadership of Colonel Joe Fletcher battled the elements in the hostile arctic environment to pave the way for a semipermanent scientific base in the center of the North Polar Basin. Today a secure and well-equipped station manned by half a dozen scientists is in active operation on that island.

Because T-3 rotates with the currents and the wind in the Polar Sea, it makes an excellent springboard for scientific research which will eventually open up the mysteries of the Polar Basin. Today we know very little more about this vast area which forms the cap of the world and represents 85 per cent of the arctic regions than was discovered by the early explorers more than half a century ago.

With the steady increase of circumpolar activities and the rapid development of transpolar aviation, this area is becoming of vital importance to man in the Western Hemisphere—as a highway of aerial communication in peace, and a barrier of defense in war.

The USAF deserves great credit for having realized the unique opportunity for scientific exploration of the Polar Basin which T-3 and the other ice islands represent.

I had the privilege of taking part in the initial phase of the ice island operation—the planning, preparation and initial landing—until the permanent station was established.

This is in part the story of our life and adventures on the ice. It is also an attempt to draw a picture, as we know it today, of the Polar Basin, the deep ocean area around the North Pole.* It is, too, an account of the nature of the polar world, of animal and human life on the enormous expanse of floating sea ice or pack ice in the North Polar Basin. Finally, as any such an account must, it tells something about the adventures and discoveries of those who went before us.

Almost 90 per cent of the population of the earth inhabits the Northern Hemisphere, and the greatest concentration of the most intelligent, and consequently most destructive, peoples is found roughly between the thirtieth and the sixtieth parallels as a circumpolar zone.

While in ancient times the known world centered around the Mediterranean Sea, today the gravity of civilization, with its most highly developed culture and power, is centered around the top of the world. In terms of modern intercontinental communications, the North Polar Basin has become the Mediterranean Sea of air transportation, for the aircraft, unlike surface transport, is free to take the shortest route, the great circle, between two points. Similarly, the aerial short cut for the destructive forces of nations at war may in the future lie over the North Polar Basin.

This means that the time has come for us to change our concept of the geography of our world. While earlier the Mercator projection produced the most practical maps, since it gave an accurate reproduction of the belt nearest the Equator, we may

---

* Also known as the Polar Sea or Arctic Ocean, the Polar Basin, two thousand miles across, is surrounded by the American, Asiatic and European continents.

today obtain a truer picture of the distribution of cultural areas and the geographical relation between the continents by studying the map in azimuthal projection.

In the tenth century Greenland incidentally became a stepping-stone to the New World in the Norsemen's erratic westward migration. Later, for many centuries the need for short northerly trade routes from Europe to the countries on the other side of the world sent men in quest of the Northeast and Northwest passages. Today the Arctic has become a link between the continents, a steppingstone in our development of air transportation, for the shortest air route between Europe and America lies across the top of the world.

The shortest route between Alaska and Scandinavia crosses the Pole, and the route from London to Tokyo across the Pole is fourteen hundred miles shorter than the route London-Cairo-Tokyo. The flight from San Francisco to Denmark over the top of the world is claimed to be twenty hours shorter than the conventional route via New York. Thus the short cut across the Pole is as important to the airways as the Panama and Suez Canals are to shipping.

It has been said that a new era in commercial aviation began on November 19, 1952, when a Scandinavian Airlines System (SAS) DC-6 Super-Cloudmaster passenger plane made the first trial run from Los Angeles, California, to Copenhagen, Denmark, via Northwest Greenland, covering almost ten thousand miles in little more than twenty-four hours. It carried among the passengers two of the pioneers in polar aviation, General Hjalmar Riiser-Larsen and Colonel Bernt Balchen.

The polar route is not only shorter, it is also preferable on account of the larger number of alternate airfields along the flight as compared with the route across the Atlantic. The arctic regions are no longer remote areas isolated from the rest of the world; they are likely in time to become the crossroads for world commerce and a factor in world domination. Close to two hundred radio and weather stations encompassing the Polar Basin, and the numerous airfields established along the rim of the Polar Sea are necessary links in the plans for the future that will safeguard tomorrow's airways across the Pole.

Defensively, the bleak territories fringing the Polar Sea will serve as bases for the operation of radar networks essential in the military control of strategic areas, guarding the roof entrance to the American continent. The Arctic is already of major importance in global strategy, for the shortest air routes between American continental bases and vital industries in central Russia pass over the Polar Basin. Furthermore, Washington, D.C., or Seattle is only 4,200 miles from the important Russian ice-free port of Murmansk, and within this range from Murmansk lies the greatest concentration of population and industries in the United States.

All of these factors underline our need to know more about the Polar Basin and the arctic lands along its rim.

North

CHAPTER ONE

Toward the Pole

L et's go," said General Old, stamping his feet in the hard-packed snow of the Greenland air base. With impatience he watched the photographers, who were determined to get one last picture of the small group of men about to take off for the ice island, T-3, close to the North Pole. This was the beginning of an expedition to establish a semipermanent scientific station in the center of the Polar Basin.

It was early in the morning of March 19, 1952. The ski-wheel-equipped twin-motored C-47 of the 10th Air Rescue, flight D, had been serviced and was ready to fly. In addition to the regular gas load it carried an auxiliary four-hundred-gallon gas tank in the fuselage. Before daybreak twelve hundred pounds of the most essential equipment had been loaded and securely strapped down in the aircraft.

The plans called for an eight o'clock take-off, with Captain Lew Erhart and Major General William D. Old, commanding general of the Alaskan Air Command, at the controls, Captain Edward Curley as navigator, and S/Sgt Howard Clohesey as flight engineer. The landing party consisted of the project officer, Colonel Joe Fletcher, Captain Mike Brinegar and myself, in addition to Mr. George Silk, *Life* photographer. Three four-engined C-54's, each loaded with six thousand pounds of equipment, were

1

to fly top cover; the first was to take off two hours behind us, and the rest at one-hour intervals. At noon we would land on a frozen lead,* in the pack ice between Greenland and Ellesmere Island, halfway from the Greenland air base to the Pole, to refuel at a gas cache which had been placed there two days previously. If all went well the escorting aircraft would catch up with us when we were again in the air, and would guide us toward the North Pole—to our target.

Only ten minutes behind schedule we said good-by to the remaining project personnel, including the assistant project officer Lieutenant Robert Danner, who had frozen his nose while waiting in the biting breeze. We climbed into the aircraft and closed the door behind us.

The pilots, the navigator and the engineer took their seats up front, while the rest of us squeezed in together with our backs braced against the wall next to the large fuselage tank. In the crowded aircraft were piled skis, snowshoes, tents, rations, arctic clothing, rifles, ammunition and other vital items of equipment which would enable us to survive for a period of ninety days under the most extreme arctic conditions. Additional equipment, some of which could be landed by parachute if necessary, was carried in the C-54's.

We were some two thousand pounds overweight, and the C-47 rattled and jerked as it started to move and taxied to the end of the snow-covered runway.

There the engines and the instruments were checked thoroughly, for we were about to embark on a most hazardous flight. Finally the engineer put his head through the doorway and shouted: "Okay?" We nodded.

The engines roared like thunder as Erhart opened the throttles,

* An open lane or water passage between large pieces of sea ice.

and the aircraft raced down the runway. Suddenly we were jerked into the air. We were on our way at last, after many months of strenuous preparation.

As in every polar expedition, there were a great many unknown factors involved, and as so often before during the past weeks, all the things that might happen passed through my mind: engine failure or other mechanical difficulties might necessitate a forced landing on the pack ice; we might fail to locate the ice island; because of our limited navigational aids, we might get lost, and fly around in circles and consume our precious fuel; we might break a ski during landing and get stuck in the center of the North Polar Basin. . . .

All these possibilities had been carefully considered, but the fact remained that we were now flying a twin-engine aircraft almost one thousand miles across the wide expanse of polar ice where navigation is exceedingly difficult, and where the chances of finding a lost aircraft are extremely slim. We traveled on a one-way ticket, so to speak, for we had hardly enough gas for the return journey. There was no alternative; every polar expedition has to count on a certain proportion of good luck.

We flew at one thousand feet to avoid the strong head wind at higher altitudes. We flew on, hour after hour, northward across the ever-changing landscape of pack ice, mountains and fjords. It was freezing in the aircraft, and I shivered in spite of my heavy arctic clothing: thick woolen garments, an arctic flying suit, fur socks and mukluks.* We stood huddled together by the wall, for it was too cold to sit down. No one spoke unless he had something essential to say. It was a perfect day, with unlimited visibility across the endless plains of snow and ice. To the left of us we saw the east coast of Ellesmere Island, its sheer mountain

* Alaskan Eskimo word for skin boots.

cliffs rising from the pack ice, with ice-bound fjords, rivers and valleys between. To the right we looked across Greenland with its snow-covered islands, its nunataks,* and its glacier arms twisting like furrowed tongues into the Polar Sea.

Below us huge glaciers ground together, avalanches boomed, and no apparent life stirred. Beyond the distant nunataks we could see the inland ice, an endless undulating sheet extending from the head of the fjords six hundred miles to the mountainous east coast of Greenland.

The Greenland Ice Cap completely covers the interior of the island, the largest on earth; only one-fifth of the entire area is free from ice. At the center the ice is over nine thousand feet thick, sloping down to less than one hundred feet at the edges. As the snow accumulates on top it is transformed into glaciers. Under the tremendous pressure which is thus constantly built up, the ice flows slowly out from the center and is squeezed down through the valleys into the sea, forming glacier arms which break off by their own weight at the end and form icebergs, which drift away from the coast by the currents.

Near the edges the uneven distribution of the pressure of the moving ice and the irregularities of the ground constantly create vertical splits in the ice, which may be shallow or may reach to the bottom of the glacier. Some of these crevasses are only a few inches wide; others are as much as fifty yards across. Drifting snow often builds bridges across the narrow crevasses, and when the bridges are concealed by newly fallen snow they form treacherous death traps for the inexperienced traveler.

In the interior of this desert of ice there is no life of any kind. Birds may cross it during their seasonal migrations, and perhaps

* Mountainous peaks jutting through the ice.

on rare occasions reindeer, hares and lemmings may attempt to traverse it.

Outside the fringes of this frozen plain, along the narrow coast line between the Polar Sea and the eternal ice, a few scattered Eskimo settlements or occasional trappers' cabins lie on the slope by the fjords.

It was here that I began my arctic work thirteen years ago. Since that time a number of scientific expeditions have taken me to many different parts of the Arctic, from Spitsbergen in the east to the western shores of Alaska.

As I was watching the interminable miles of arctic wastes flow by, thinking of the task ahead, I was grateful for the experiences which I had gained in the past when I traveled alone with my dogs along the seemingly endless arctic coast, over frozen fjords, through valleys to the sea, across hummocks and pack ice, and glaciers with treacherous crevasses at the fringe of the Ice Cap.

In spite of the hard, unromantic life of a winter completely cut off from civilization by more than a hundred miles of impenetrable pack ice, the Arctic has a fascination which is difficult to describe. He who has once watched the first sign of the returning sun in spring after months of almost complete darkness always longs to be back among these enormous wastes of ice and snow. Perhaps it is the same instinct that urges the migratory birds to leave the warmth of the southern sun every spring, and fly north to the magic nights of the Polar circle; or the same desire that once led our forefathers—the Norsemen—to leave behind all they possessed and the security of their native homesteads to explore and exploit unknown land beyond the barrier of frozen seas.

In the Arctic one meets many kinds of people from almost every walk of life. Some have been driven into the frozen desert

by the brutal struggle for survival; some have come to escape
from the difficulties of civilization and its social complications;
others to realize their dreams of adventure, or in search of scientific knowledge. Whatever their motivations, know-how and
practical experience are essential to survival; and in almost every
case the spirit of adventure is a factor of importance, for the
success of an arctic traveler depends as much upon his mental
attitude as on his physical stamina.

When I happened to be chosen to accompany the T-3 expedition to the North Polar Basin as its civilian scientist, it was
mainly because I had done similar things before. Through previous scientific expeditions to the North I was familiar with the
conditions we could expect to encounter on T-3.

I started with the advantage of having been brought up as a
child in northern Norway, and thereafter continued to learn the
facts of arctic living the hard way. During the entire summer of
1939, I was a member of the expedition organized by the well-
known Swedish glaciologist, Professor Ahlmann, to Fröya Glacier
on Clavering Island, Greenland, and throughout the following
year I continued his glaciological studies. For fourteen months
I lived with two arctic trappers in a small laboratory we had
established in a trapper's cabin on the barren coast of Northeast
Greenland on the edge of the inland ice, completely cut off from
the rest of the world. I had the good luck of sharing the chances
of fortune with companions who were veterans of the North,
and who gave me a thorough lesson in arctic survival. One of
them, Henry Rudi, had spent twenty years of his life in the
Arctic, in Spitsbergen, Greenland, Franz Josef Land and Jan
Mayen. He had shot over seven hundred polar bears, and seen
his own brother killed by a wounded walrus in the icy water off
Spitsbergen. During this period I came to know well the dangers

of glacial ice. I was also thoroughly acquainted with the nature of the pack ice, for I had traveled through and been caught in the drifting sea ice on many occasions. Once, in 1941, I spent three months on board a sealing vessel in the drift ice east of Newfoundland and Labrador, studying the biology of seals.

As a member of the Danish Pearyland Expedition in 1947 I was among the first group of eight men who landed with a Catalina flying boat at the northern end of Greenland to explore the comparatively unknown interior of Pearyland. During the expedition we learned much about the hazards of airborne operations in the Arctic.

For two years preceding the T-3 expedition I had been in charge of extensive field expeditions in Alaska as a member of the staff of the USAF Arctic Aeromedical Laboratory, concerned with various problems relating to man in the Arctic. In addition I happened to be a physician, which Colonel Fletcher felt might come in handy in case of any accidents or casualties during the T-3 operations. Otherwise Joe Fletcher was skeptical of physicians since the time his doctor took two hours removing his appendix; so he probably placed greater value on the circumstance that my particular field of work during the last fifteen years had been arctic physiology, and especially nutrition. This gave him someone to whom he could delegate responsibility for the diet.

There is a distinct advantage in taking part in arctic expeditions composed of scientists from different fields, where success is always dependent on each man's helping the others. One is called upon to assist the geographer in his surveying, to carry stones for the geologist, to take observations in the absence of the meteorologist, to collect specimens for the biologist, and to turn the winch for the oceanographer. Thus quite apart from the results gained in one's own subject, one is also bound to learn something about branches of science other than one's own. This is particularly important for the student of the human factors in the Arctic, for man in the arctic environment is greatly affected by biology, geography, climatology and even oceanography. To be able to understand the problems confronting man in the arctic world, therefore, some knowledge of these fields is very necessary.

CHAPTER TWO

Pioneers of the Polar Basin

The importance of the T-3 project, what was entailed in setting up a base on a floating island of ice in the center of the Polar Basin, the risks that had to be faced and the problems that had to be solved, cannot be understood or realized unless the reader has some background knowledge of previous polar exploration and of the nature of the North Polar Basin.

Everything we knew about the geography and nature of the Polar Sea and the problems of survival that it posed—all the information on which the members of our expedition were now staking their lives and hopes for success—was dangerously and laboriously gathered over the past century by a few incredibly determined and courageous pioneers.

In the earliest times the scholars fancied that beyond the regions inhabited by man there was a realm of darkness and fog, where land, sea and sky fused together into a fluid mass ending in the abyss at the edge of the earth.

However, the existence of the frozen sea far to the north at the end of the earth was known to the ancient Greeks long before the beginning of the Christian era. Pytheas, the Greek from Massila, sailed through the Pillars of Hercules in the year 350 B.C. and continued on to the north. According to the legends he reached Iceland, which he named Thule, and may have seen the pack ice east of Greenland in the fog. The Vikings touched the fringes of the frozen sea on their early voyages in open wooden boats in the ninth and tenth centuries, and encountered nature in one of her fiercest moods. They became well acquainted with the nature of the pack ice. In the famous Norse King's Mirror, written in the year 1240 or 1260, the unknown author gives a vivid and detailed description of the pack ice and its drift, and of the formation of icebergs, with dramatic accounts of men who were caught in the pack. Some of them drifted with the ice to the south and perished; others pulled their boats across the floes and eventually reached land on the east coast of Greenland.

Throughout the centuries that followed, the pack ice remained an impenetrable barrier which preserved the secrets of the vast unknown regions of the Arctic, annihilating or turning back determined and daring seafarers who challenged its bulwarks beyond "Ultima Thule," the extreme point among the known lands.

Not until the end of the nineteenth century did the veil enwrapping the central Arctic Ocean begin to lift, through the superhuman efforts of inquisitive persons such as De Long, Nansen and Peary. But still the heart of the Polar Sea remained a mystery, and even as late as the early part of the twentieth century eminent authorities believed in the existence of a great arctic continent in the Polar Sea north of Alaska.

In spite of the success of men like Nansen and Peary, knowledge was slow in accumulating and remained incomplete as long as man was obliged to travel on the surface of the earth. In Nansen's own account of his toilsome journey on foot over the drift ice toward the Pole in 1895 we read how he wished he could wing his way across the never-ending ramparts of pack ice, fissures, leads and slush ice. It was not until his dream became a reality, with the development of modern long-range aircraft, that the entire North Polar Basin, shorn of its terrible obstacles, was opened and exposed to the curiosity of man.

Sitting in the aircraft plowing its way toward the Pole, and enjoying a cup of hot coffee from the thermos jug, I could not refrain from thinking of the pioneers who struggled across the ice to the Pole. Only those who have tried to blaze their trail on foot through the jumble of heavy polar pack ice can fully appreciate the efforts and the spirit of those determined men who toiled across the floes floating on the deep Polar Sea. Day after day, carrying heavy loads, they pressed toward the unknown, in front of exhausted dogs, pulling the sledges over the interminable chaos of ice, climbing over hummocks which blocked their advance, wading through snowdrifts and slush ice up to their knees, running for their lives across treacherous new ice covering the leads between the floes, and making detours several miles long in order to advance only a few hundred yards. And then the heartbreaking discovery that after having walked all day, the current, while they slept at night, had brought them back to where they started.

The saga of the central Polar Basin began with the classic pioneer drift of the *Fram* under Fridtjof Nansen across the Polar Sea, 1893-1896.

Men had tried to penetrate into the heart of the Polar Sea before. Mention should be made of Parry and De Long. In 1827, Sir Edward Parry, an Englishman, made a dash toward the Pole on foot from a base on Spitsbergen, with twenty-seven men to haul his two heavy sledges—boats equipped with steel runners—across the frozen sea ice. After thirty days' struggle with the ice and open water he had reached a point only 150 miles north of his base, with another 435 miles to go. The swiftly moving ice carried him southward almost as fast as he advanced to the north. Retreat was therefore inevitable.

Then, in the 1870's there was George Washington De Long, a commander in the American Navy. De Long believed in a Japanese current running north through Bering Strait and along the east coast of Wrangel Land. He knew from the whalers' experiences that whenever their vessels were stuck in the ice there, they would drift northward. With the help of what he therefore assumed was a north-running current, he hoped to reach the Pole. However, his ship, the *Jeannette*, was locked in the ice in September, 1879, southeast of Wrangel Land, and drifted with the ice in a west-northwesterly direction for two years, with the crew helpless prisoners, until the summer of 1881, when the ship was crushed and sank. The crew were forced to make for land, and only a few, who eventually reached the Lena delta in East Siberia, survived.

When relics from the wrecked *Jeannette* were found frozen into the ice by an Eskimo in southwest Greenland three years later, it was apparent that they must have been carried on a floe right across the Polar Sea. This conclusion formed the basis for Nansen's plans, for he figured that if an ice floe could drift clear across this unknown region, he should be able to take advantage of that drift in polar exploration.

On September 25, 1893, the four-hundred-ton *Fram*, specially built to withstand the tremendous pressure of the ice, was frozen in the pack ice north of the New Siberian Islands, after having sailed from Norway and plowed her way in among the ice as far north as possible. On board were thirteen men, equipped with the best of clothing and five years' provisions. This was the beginning of a thirty-five months' drift which was to take them across the Polar Sea until they escaped from the grip of the ice northwest of Spitsbergen on August 13, 1896.

At the start, when the ship was firmly locked in the ice, the rudder was dismantled to keep it from being destroyed by the pressure of the ice. The ship was converted into winter quarters, and the drift began at the approach of the first winter nights. On board the ice-locked ship the crew lived and worked like a family, engaging in active research, making continuous scientific observations, and sharing the burdens of the monotonous everyday work. Every other day, on the basis of their astronomical observations, they plotted their position on the white map as they advanced.

The sun rose and sank until it finally vanished for good at the onset of the winter night, leaving only a flaming reflection in the southern sky. The drift continued among the formless blue shadows of the arctic nights over the ice fields, with the light of the restless aurora waving its veil of glittering silver and ever-changing colors, yellow, green, red, across the vault of the sky.

Up to October, 1895, the general drift was west and north until they reached a point roughly 250 miles from the Pole. From this point they drifted in a more southerly direction, away from the Pole.

At times the ice jammed and yielded to the pressure of the sea, shaking and lifting the ship with a deafening roar. The roar would start as a thundering rumble as from an earthquake far away. As the echoes from the thunder came nearer, the ice would crack in all directions, piling up all around the ship and breaking in on the deck, crackling, moaning and grinding against the rig and the sides. The *Fram* would tremble as it was tossed about among the packing ice rising on the tidal waves.

On a few occasions they thought they might have to abandon the ship, so they slept fully dressed, with everything in readiness to be moved onto the ice.

In the course of the first winter it became clear that the drift might not take the *Fram* across the Pole after all. With the coming of spring, and apparently spurred by the inactive monotony of the life on board the ice-bound ship, Nansen began to play with the idea of trying to reach the Pole with his dogs and sledges. During his daily expeditions, he constantly studied the condition of the ice and his prospects of being able to make his way across it.

With the approach of the second winter, his plans became firmer. By November, 1894, he had made up his mind. Having carefully weighed every factor involved, and considered every possible hazard during many sleepless nights, he had decided to stake everything on a northward march over the ice.

On March 14, 1895, Nansen, accompanied by Lieutenant Hjalmar Johansen, left the *Fram* at 84° 04′ N., 102° E. (360 nautical miles south of the Pole*). They planned to penetrate the polar pack ice as far north as possible, to explore the regions toward the Pole, beyond the passage of the *Fram*, and then to make the return journey home to Norway by dogs and sledge via the Franz Josef Archipelago, a remote group of islands northeast of Spitsbergen and north of Eurasia.

Traveling on skis, the two men wandered for months across large expanses of flat ice, of pressure ridges and hummocks, into the unknown. To start with, the ice appeared to get more even the farther north they advanced, allowing them to make fourteen miles or more in a day. But soon the mishaps began, and their clothing and gear became increasingly heavier from the accumulated moisture which froze in the severe cold. The impassability of the rugged ice, the continual lifting of the heavily loaded sledges, frostbite and the struggle against the bitter cold all

---

* There are 60 nautical miles to a degree of latitude, and since 90° N. is the Pole, a point close to 84° N. would be roughly 360 miles south of the Pole.

combined to slow their progress. They were forced to start killing some of their dogs, feeding the carcasses to the others. Exhausted toward the end of a day's journey, they sometimes fell asleep as they stumbled along, only to awaken as they suddenly pitched forward on their skis. At night they would find a shelter from the wind behind a hummock or a ridge of ice, eating their pemmican heated over the primus stove, and then crawling into the icy sleeping bags to thaw their clothes, and to rest. Their garments were so stiff from frozen moisture condensed in the course of the march that the sleeves of their coats rubbed deep sores in their wrists.

The march went on, mile after mile, across ridge after ridge; the men driving their dogs ahead, pulling the sledges with them, becoming hardened as the days passed, until only brutality and hard-hearted self-preservation remained.

Eventually it became clear that the ice was drifting southward almost as fast as they advanced to the north, for observation after observation revealed that they were not making any significant progress northward.

On the evening of April 8, having reached 86° 13′ N., 95° E., Nansen decided to turn back and to make for land.

Then began a dramatic retreat almost unequaled in the saga of the North. For months, on small rations, they staggered south across the ice, which became worse as they approached open water. One after another the exhausted dogs gave in and were killed with a knife or strangled to save ammunition. The men were so tired that when they fell they wanted only to lie there in the snow to save themselves the trouble of standing up again.

As they eventually approached the limits of the drift ice, noticing the ice rise and sink with the swell, they began scanning the horizon impatiently for land. It was here that Nansen wrote:

"There are moments when it seems impossible that any creature not possessed of wings can get farther, and one longingly follows the flight of a passing gull, and thinks how far away one would soon be could one borrow its wings."

They stumbled on with inconceivable toil, paddling across the leads, sometimes trailed by hungry bears, one of which almost killed Johansen, and when they reached the dark surface of the sea they sacrificed the last two surviving dogs. Here they took to their kajaks, which they had pulled so many miles on the sledges, and on August 14, after having fought their way to the extremities of the polar pack ice through slush ice and water in the thaw, they landed on one of the islands in the Franz Josef Archipelago. Here they wintered in a stone hut, maintaining health and fitness for a period of nine months on nothing but meat and blubber from walrus and polar bears. They slept on a shelf of stones, and cooked their meals by a blubber oil lamp.

By a coincidence, as they were about to set off across the sea to Spitsbergen in their kajaks, they met the British explorer Frederick Jackson north of Cape Flora on June 7, 1896. As they approached Jackson, the first representative of the outside world they had seen for three years, Nansen raised his hat and said: "How do you do?"!

On August 13 the same year, the *Fram*, which in the meantime had continued its drift, was finally extricated from the ice with dynamite, and reached Norway simultaneously with Nansen.

Nansen had proved his theory about the transpolar current. He and his men had discovered the deep North Polar Basin, and concluded that no land could exist to the north of the known Eurasian archipelagos, Spitsbergen, Franz Josef Land, Taimir Peninsula and the New Siberian Islands, which lie on the fringe of the continental shelf surrounding the Polar Basin. But above

all, they brought back a wealth of scientific information and observations on the temperatures and salinity of the water, the
biology of the Polar Sea, the distribution of the ocean currents,
the formation of ice and the effect of wind on the movement of
sea ice.

While Nansen and his companion were retreating to their
island shelter, another retreat was taking place on the opposite
side of the Pole. It was Lieutenant (USN) Peary's race against
hunger and death across the northern Ice Cap of Greenland.

This brilliant arctic traveler, whose life ambition was to attain
the geographical North Pole, had returned to the North year
after year in the pursuit of this goal, which had beckoned to him
ever since 1886 when he went to Greenland on a general reconnaissance expedition.

His approach to the Pole via Greenland was apparently based
on the belief popular at the time that Greenland extended northward all the way to the Pole, and that, therefore, it could be
reached overland.

In 1891 he led an expedition to Northwest Greenland but broke
his leg while exploring the inland ice and was forced to return
to his base. In the spring of 1892 he set out once more on a
journey across the Ice Cap and reached the northern limits of the
inland ice of Greenland, from where he believed he could see
the Arctic Ocean beyond. He went on to the east until he reached
the mountains forming the eastern limit of the Ice Cap, and on
July 4 he looked down from Navy Cliff into Independence Fjord,
Northeast Greenland, and discovered Pearyland beyond it, which
he thought was separated from Greenland by a channel. He returned to his base after an absence of eighty days, having covered
a distance of fourteen hundred miles.

The following year he went back to Greenland again and re-

mained until 1895. In the spring of that year he once more succeeded in crossing the inland ice in an attempt to explore further
the new land he had discovered. He got as far as Independence
Fjord, and barely made it back to his base, where he arrived after
a dramatic retreat with nothing more than four biscuits left as
food.

From now on Peary adopted a different plan for his attack on
the North Pole, using Ellesmere Island as a staging base for a
northward dash across the sea ice. In 1898 he sailed north through
Smith Sound, but was blocked in his advance by the ice, and was
forced to set up winter quarters on the east coast of Ellesmere
Island. From this base he began preparations for his northward
journey, establishing food depots along the coast. However, on a
sledge journey during the winter both his feet were frostbitten,
and his companions had to carry him back to the base, where
eight of his toes were amputated.

In spite of this, in the spring of 1900, he set out on a sledge
journey around the north coast of Greenland to determine once
and for all its exact northern limits. He reached the north coast
of Pearyland and proved conclusively that Greenland is a single
island, the northern extremity of which he had traced on the
map. Thus the possibility of an overland route to the Pole through
Greenland was definitely ruled out.

After his return to the base preparations were continued
through the year 1901 for an attempt to push north from Ellesmere Island to the Pole.

On April 1, 1902, Peary left from Cape Hecla on Ellesmere
Island on his first long journey over "the great ice" of the Arctic
Ocean, only to learn that he had started too late in the season.
Huge pressure ridges, masses of ice rubble, open channels and

deep snow made the advance almost impossible. On April 21 he therefore turned back at 84° 17′ N.

He tried again in 1905, when he arrived with the *Roosevelt*, skippered by Bob Bartlett, at Cape Sheridan on Ellesmere Island late in the summer. There he wintered and prepared for the sledge journey to the Pole. He came closer to the Pole than Nansen had, but had to turn back at 87° N. (180 miles from the Pole), and barely made it to the base late in the spring of 1906.

Three years later Peary tried again, and this time he succeeded —after twenty-three years of arctic work. From Cape Columbia on Ellesmere Island, the northernmost extremity of the land, he set out on March 1 across the ice to the Pole, along the same track which we were to fly forty-three years later, with his Negro companion Matt Henson, Ootah, the faithful Eskimo who had marched with him to 87° N. in 1906, and three other Eskimo helpers. The North Pole was reached on April 6 at ten o'clock in the morning. They spent thirty-six hours at the Pole, then started the return journey on April 7, and reached land at Cape Columbia in sixteen days.

People have wondered how it was possible during their return journey to cover such great distances—413 nautical miles—in such a short time. In his narrative Peary quotes his Eskimo companion Ootah, who gave the answer: "The devil was asleep or having trouble with his wife, or we should never have come back so easily."

Today Ootah, the only surviving member of the polar party, is a very old man, but he is still five feet eight inches tall and as sturdy as ever. I saw him in Greenland shortly before we took off to fly to the Pole. Dressed in his bearskin parka and trousers, with kamiks* of caribou and sealskin, he was standing in front

* Greenland Eskimo word for skin boots.

of his winter house upon the hill by the fjord overlooking the ice to the north. As he spoke, he pointed with a stick of driftwood across the icebergs locked in the fjord ice.

He could still remember the marches through the fog and biting winds when he tramped along with Peary to break the virgin trail over the endless ice away from the land, for a purpose obscure to the Eskimos. Their motivation was the great treasure that Peary had promised those of the Eskimos who would go to the farthest point with him: whale boat, rifle, shotgun, ammunition and knives.

Ootah spoke slowly, but eventually I could piece together the story as he had seen it.

They had started off from land with 26 men, 140 dogs and 28 sledges, and depots were placed out on the ice in igloos by supporting parties. Five days' journey out from the land they were stopped by a broad lane of open water, where they camped and waited for five days for the lead to close. Here some of the Eskimos lost faith and went back to the land. Finally, as the lead did not close, Peary and his men had to ferry their dogs and sledges across the water on rafts of ice cut by axes from the edge of the floe. At the end of the twenty-eighth day of the journey, a channel broke open in the middle of their igloo camp, and half the party drifted away for a while on the floe that broke loose.

At 88° N. the last of the supporting parties returned to land. Peary, Matt Henson, Ootah and the three Eskimo helpers, with five sledges and forty dogs, moved on, crossing new ice so thin that it buckled beneath the weight of their sledges.

On the last day Peary twice traveled back and forth with a light sledge full of instruments to find the Pole. Before they returned five flags were planted in the ice at the top of the world.

Then they gave three cheers with Henson leading. To the Eskimos the only thing of importance was the fact that now they could turn and hurry home.

Peary had found the Pole to be nothing but pack ice over a tremendous depth of water.

As the news of Peary's having reached the Pole was flashed across the world, Roald Amundsen was in the middle of gathering financial support for his proposed transpolar expedition. He had already, in the *Gjöa*, conquered the Northwest Passage—the northern sea route from the Atlantic to the Pacific, thus bringing the epic of the Northwest Passage to a victorious end after four centuries of search and sacrifice. His new plans, which he presented in 1908, had originally involved an attack on the Polar Basin from Bering Strait in Nansen's *Fram*. With provisions for five years he would press northward as far as possible, awaiting the most favorable moment to join the moving ice in its drift across the Pole. He intended to enter the drift ice further east than Nansen had.

Various circumstances beyond his control forced him to alter his plans. Finally, in July, 1918, he sailed north from Norway in the *Maud*, with the well-known Norwegian oceanographer, Dr. H. U. Sverdrup, in charge of the scientific program of the expedition. In September they passed Cape Chelyuskin in Siberia, and fixed its position as the most northerly point of Asia. They were compelled to spend two winters north of Siberia, and reached Nome in the fall of 1920. Thus, Amundsen was the first man to make both the Northeast and the Northwest Passage, that is, to pass north of both the Eurasian and American continents.

In 1922, Sverdrup sailed in the *Maud* from Seattle, once more bound for the Polar Basin. This time he spent three years locked in the sea ice north of eastern Siberia, the drift of the ship coinciding fairly closely with that of the *Jeannette.* He returned to Nome in the fall of 1925, having reached a northernmost point of 76° 25′ N.

During all those years much valuable information was added to our knowledge of the Polar Basin. One of the most important conclusions of the expedition was that no extensive land masses existed in the (at that time) unexplored part of the Polar Basin, a conclusion which has since been amply substantiated. Sverdrup also realized that the exploration of the Polar Basin could be accomplished more efficiently from the air.

Three years later, therefore, he presented detailed plans for the establishment of a semipermanent scientific station on the drift ice in the central Polar Basin, to be supplied and maintained by airship. His presentation was published in 1928, and on the basis of our present knowledge it appears very sound indeed. It is regrettable that such plans never materialized until the Russians landed by air near the North Pole and actually established a station on the drift ice.

From Rudolf Island, the northernmost island of the Franz Josef Archipelago, a squadron of four-engined Russian aircraft took off for the Pole, on May 21, 1937, and landed Papanin and his three companions on an ice floe in the vicinity of the Pole (89° 26′ N., 87° W.). For 274 days they drifted in zigzags with the current. When they were taken off the floe by an icebreaker in February, 1938, as they were drifting into the Atlantic Ocean east of Greenland, they had covered a distance of twelve hundred miles, and had made numerous hydrological, magnetical and meteorological observations.

A similar drift, although involuntary, was made by the Russian icebreaker *Sedov* in 1937-1940, with fifteen men aboard, who drifted with the ice for twenty-six months, following very nearly the same route as Nansen's *Fram* from the New Siberian Islands to Spitsbergen. The *Sedov* was one of three Russian icebreakers which were caught in the ice while engaged in a routine mission along the Siberian coast in the fall of 1937. While the icebreakers *Sadko* and *Malygin* escaped from the ice in August, 1938, the *Sedov* remained ice-bound until rescued by the powerful ice-breaker *Josef Stalin*. During the drift Nansen's measurements of the deep Polar Basin were confirmed.

By this time the general picture of the North Polar regions was taking final shape. The northern extremities of the land along the border of the polar pack ice had been traced in on the white map of the Polar Basin. The details of the nature of the interior were still lacking, however. This was the scientific justification for our ice island expedition in the spring of 1952, for only by the use of aircraft was it possible to approach effectively the tremendous task of exploring the central North Polar region.

Polar flying with landings on sea ice is an art of its own, which still has been mastered only by the few—the pioneers who are paving the way for tomorrow's commercial airways across the top of the world from one continent to another.

It began in 1897 with S. A. Andrée, the first of the polar avia-tors, who made the disastrous attempt to guide his balloon, the *Eagle*, from Spitsbergen to the North Pole. He took off on July 11, 1897, together with two Swedish companions, Strindberg and Fränkel, hoping wind and weather would carry him across the Pole. The dramatic sixty-five-hour flight came to an abrupt end when, after a series of mishaps including severe icing, they crashed on an ice floe, two hundred miles northwest of Franz Josef Land.

For twelve days they marched over the ice toward Franz Josef Land, hoping to reach the emergency depot of food and equipment they had previously established there. Wind and current carried them away from their goal, so they set their course for a small group of islands in the Spitsbergen Archipelago. For another forty days they toiled on across the slack summer ice. Exhausted and ill, they were forced to give in to the elements and settled on an ice floe to spend the winter in the Polar Sea.

On September 17, however, they sighted land. Their ice floe split right through the camp but they survived this and succeeded in landing on the southwest side of the small glaciated White Island in the Spitsbergen Archipelago on October 2. On this inhospitable island of ice and stones they attempted to survive through the winter, but perished in the numbing cold and the killing blizzards. Strindberg was the first to die; he was buried among the rocks by his companions. The bodies of all three men were found thirty-three years later. During all those years their tragedy remained a secret buried with their diaries in the ice. On the basis of their recovered records, Hans W:son Ahlmann has written a dramatic account of this tragic expedition. The actual cause of their death has been the subject of much speculation. Carbon monoxide poisoning has been considered probable in the case of Fränkel and Andrée, for they were found lying on the floor of an unfinished shelter of stones, outside their sleeping bags, and the primus stove, which was standing on a shelf of stones between them, was half full of fuel and appeared to have been left burning. In view of the recent findings of trichinella in the flesh of a polar bear they had shot, it has been claimed that they might have died from trichinosis. The fact remains that the party was doomed to perish from exposure, lack of clothing, equipment and experience. It seems probable that a number of factors, including trichinosis and carbon monoxide poisoning, merely hastened the fatal conclusion of this drama.

In 1914, Lieutenant Nagurski, a Russian, made his first airplane flight in the arctic regions from Novaya Zemlya, north of Siberia. In the early twenties various exploratory flights followed, both in the European and American Arctic.

On May 21, 1925, Roald Amundsen and his companions, including Hjalmar Riiser-Larsen, attempted to fly to the North Pole in two Dornier flying boats from Kings Bay, Spitsbergen. During the take-off from the fjord ice, one of the aircraft was damaged, but the flight was continued in spite of engine trouble in both airplanes. Close to 88° N., slightly more than 120 miles from the North Pole, they were forced to land in an open lead in order to fix their position. The damaged aircraft had to be abandoned, and for three weeks the six men constantly fought to save the other one from being destroyed by the pressure of the pack ice (they eventually had managed to pull it up on the floe). Eight unsuccessful attempts were made to take off. Finally by June 15 they had made a fifteen-hundred-foot strip by stamping down the deep wet snow with their feet, and knocking off hummocks with their fists. This was their last chance, and as if by a miracle the take-off succeeded. During the return flight one of the wires to the rudder broke, and they made a forced landing in the ice-filled sea at Brandy Bay on the north coast of Northeast Land, Spitsbergen.

The following year Richard E. Byrd flew from Spitsbergen to the Pole and returned in fifteen and a half hours without incident. Later Roald Amundsen in the airship *Norge* made the first transpolar flight from Spitsbergen to Alaska. As he came sailing in over an Eskimo settlement at low altitude he shouted a greeting to the gazing natives on the ground. They thought that the world had come to an end, for now "whales were flying through the sky and God himself had spoken from a basket up under the belly of the whale."

In the spring of 1937 the Russians made a total of thirteen aircraft landings on the sea ice in the Polar Basin, in support of Ivan Papanin's group on the ice floe. In recent years little has been heard of Russian efforts in polar aviation.

The daily stunts of pioneer bush pilots in Alaska and Canada have become famous. In addition, the U.S. Air Force and Navy have been carrying out extensive joint air operations with landings on the sea ice north of Alaska ever since 1949. Most of these landings, by twin-engined aircraft, were made by our pilot, Captain Lew Erhart, in the same C-47 in which we were to fly across the North Polar Basin on the T-3 expedition.

CHAPTER THREE

The Polar Basin

The Polar Basin, as seen from the air, is nothing but endless wastes of floating ice, sweeping with the wind and currents across the deep sea water. In March, the ice is heavy and coarse, with high pressure ridges and hummocks covered with snow, and with only a few open leads between the floes.

It is a common misconception that all of the arctic regions are like this—a desolate, inhospitable no man's land of snow and ice, where human existence is impossible.

People fail to realize that human beings, such as the Eskimos, have survived in parts of the arctic region for thousands of years, apparently in relative comfort and without too many problems until the white race gave them access to civilization.

The word "Arctic" is derived from the Greek word *arktos,* which stands for the northern constellation the Great Bear, and applies to the area of land and sea nearest to the North Pole. The southern boundary of the arctic lands follows in a general way the northern limits of the tree line. According to the standard definition the arctic regions include the areas where the mean temperature for the warmest month is below +50° F., and which have an average temperature below +32° F. for the coldest month. On the basis of this definition the arctic regions include northern Alaska, a large part of the Canadian archipelago, all of

Greenland, Spitsbergen and other eastern arctic islands, the
northern fringe of Norway, and northern Siberia.

Though almost half of Norway lies north of the Arctic Circle,*
thanks to the Gulf Stream the conditions in the northern extremity (which may be said to lie within the "arctic region")
are not essentially different from some of the more southerly parts
of that country.

In Spitsbergen conditions are far more severe, with an unfavorable climate, exceedingly difficult terrain, and a long period
of winter darkness. On the other hand, both land and sea offer
an abundant animal life, sufficient to support human beings in
some numbers. The permanent inhabitants include several thousand coal miners.

Greenland represents practically all variations of arctic conditions. Its northern extremity, Pearyland, is the part of our
earth closest to the North Pole, while the southern point, Cape
Farewell, has the same latitude as Oslo, the capital of Norway.
As I have said, four-fifths of this largest island on earth is covered with eternal lifeless ice. Pearyland, though very nearly free
of ice, supports only a humble vegetation. The climate is dry,
like that of a desert, and sand storms, extreme cold and violent
gales, combined with five long months of winter darkness, make
outdoor activities almost impossible. In the southernmost parts
of Greenland, however, the climate is quite favorable, with fairly
mild summers and dry cold winters. The fauna is very rich, and
includes a large number of land mammals of great importance in
the economy of Eskimos and whites. In the fjords along the coast
there is an abundance of seal and fish, and the rivers are rich in
salmon.

The Canadian Arctic consists of a multitude of islands and a

* The Arctic Circle has no practical meaning—it is simply the line north
of which one may see the midnight sun; the 66½ parallel of latitude (66°
30′ N.).

long arctic coast where conditions largely are similar to the corresponding areas of Greenland.

In Alaska there is the arctic coast in the north, with scattered Eskimo settlements and a climate similar to that of the other arctic coastal regions. The arctic tundra stretches from the Polar Sea to the huge mountain range, the Brooks Range, beyond which there are immense forests rich in game, and, in the interior finally, cultivated land.

The remainder of the arctic lands consists of the arctic zone of Siberia, a closed land of islands and tundra. The eastern part of arctic Siberia is similar in climate to northern Alaska. Northern Siberia has a typically cold arctic summer; in winter the temperature decreases markedly as one goes inland from the coast.

The greater part of the arctic regions is taken up by the Polar Basin, which covers almost three million square miles, with depths exceeding fifteen thousand feet. The central portion of the Basin is a relatively lifeless desert of floating ice, moving with the wind and the current from the American and Asiatic continents north across the Pole and then to the south. Here there are no possibilities whatever for permanent human settlement. In the periphery of this area of drifting ice, however, there is considerable animal life, and in particular an abundance of seal. It is along these fringes of the pack ice that the sealing takes place in the spring, on certain sealing fields where the herds gather annually to breed.

The North Polar Basin, which is an elongated depression in the sea bed surrounded by a wide continental shelf, lies eccentric to the Pole, its center toward Alaska. The major axis runs from Spitsbergen to Alaska and is about sixteen hundred miles long. The continental shelf extends up to five hundred miles from the shores, with very shallow water, often no more than ten fathoms deep. On this shelf lie numerous groups of islands: Greenland,

Spitsbergen, Franz Josef Land, Novaya Zemlya and the Canadian
arctic islands. No islands exist in the interior of the deep Polar
Basin, although the history of early exploration is rich in tales of
land having been observed. This is not too surprising, for in those
early days it was believed that the unknown polar waters were
as shallow as the sea over the continental shelf.

The interior of the North Polar Basin has not as yet been ac-
curately charted, for it is not navigable by ship, and the pack ice
is not suitable for surface transportation. Nansen's discovery of
this deep basin was the major geographical contribution of the
Fram expedition; since that time our detailed knowledge of its
extent has accumulated but slowly, although the boundaries of
the Polar Sea are now fairly well explored. Peary failed to reach
bottom at 9,000 feet, five miles from the Pole in 1909, and in
1937 the Papanin group measured 11,500 feet near the geographical North Pole, and recorded depths of 14,000 feet several places
along their track. Even greater depths were recorded during the
Sedov drift, 1937-1940, north of Spitsbergen and Franz Josef
Land.

Detailed information about the nature of the Polar Sea is avail-
able only from the Siberian-European side of the North Polar
Basin, and the greater part of the region to the north of the
American continent is still unknown.

The origin of the Polar Basin is not clear, but it appears that it
is a relatively recent feature of the earth's surface which did not
exist in Paleozoic times. The geologists believe that the wide
continental shelf is probably a plain worn by the action of the
waves, aided by the disintegrating power of frost. This would
mean that there must have been a change in the relative level of
land and sea—either a sinking of land or rising of the sea.

Through the wide gap between Spitsbergen and Greenland

an exchange of water results from the surface outflow of cold water of low salinity (Nansen's "genuine polar water") and a simultaneous inflow of warmer water of greater salinity from the Atlantic Ocean, pouring into the Polar Basin at greater depths.

Arctic surface waters are relatively light, on account of their low salinity—due both to lack of evaporation and to the steady inflow of great volumes of fresh water from the Eurasian and American rivers. The light surface layers tend to spread outward, like an overflow from a constricted basin to which the inflow of rivers is considerable and loss of water through evaporation is slight.

Within the Polar Basin the surface waters are slowly moving across from Alaska and Siberia toward Spitsbergen and Greenland on the opposite side. Most of this water and the ice which it carries escapes into the Barents Sea and the Norwegian Sea, southwest of Spitsbergen, where it forms the East Greenland Current, flowing southward along the east coast of Greenland. Some of it finds its way out of the Polar Basin through Smith Sound and other channels west of Greenland and feeds the Labrador Current along the west side of Davis Strait. Finally some of the water escapes westward through the Beaufort Sea and merges again in the great transpolar drift, except for a small portion which flows to the south in Bering Strait.

The East Greenland Current splits, sending one branch eastward to the north of Iceland and the Faeroes. The other branch rounds Cape Farewell and flows northward into Davis Strait. On the Grand Banks of Newfoundland the Labrador Current meets the Gulf Stream.

The Arctic Ocean receives much more water than it loses by evaporation. As the Polar Basin is essentially an enclosed sea, it would be completely clogged with ice formed by the freezing of the sea were it not for the fact that an estimated quantity of twenty-six billion square yards of ice annually escapes to the south, mainly with the East Greenland Current.

This south-going current, because of the rotation of the earth which in the Northern Hemisphere deflects all free-moving bodies to the right of their original motion, is forced toward the east coast of Greenland, causing the pack ice to pile up all along the shoreline.

The main influx of water into the Polar Basin consists of a submerging branch of the Gulf Stream system, which enters the Polar Sea north of Spitsbergen. This water of Atlantic origin moves clear across the Polar Basin, for it is found to the north of the New Siberian Islands, as shown by measurements of temperature and salinity taken by the *Fram* and *Sedov* expeditions.

It has been well known since the time of the first circumnavigators that surface currents depend in general on the prevailing wind, the configuration of the coast and the contours of the bottom. The ice, too, is driven mainly by the wind, except near land where local conditions, such as promontories, rivers, tides and currents may make a difference. It moves roughly at about one-fiftieth the speed of the wind and veers approximately thirty degrees to the right of the direction of the wind, owing to the rotation of the earth.

As Nansen pointed out, the oceanographical conditions of the North Polar Basin exert a great influence upon the climate of the area, and changes in the circulation of the ice and water would greatly affect the climate of the regions surrounding it. The warm currents flowing north are essential to the growth of the marine organisms on which animal life in the Polar Sea subsists. The cold southbound currents and the ice they carry are the main obstacles to navigation in polar waters, and exert a decisive influence upon the climate of the arctic lands.

The circulation of ice and water also explains the wide range of conditions encountered in the different parts of the arctic regions, where ice formation, climate, animal life, habitation and natural food resources vary greatly. In arctic Norway the warm Gulf Stream has created conditions favorable to human existence —a luxuriant vegetation, an abundance of animal life and some of the world's largest fishing banks. The cold arctic currents sweeping along the shores of Greenland have brought this island today to a stage of development similar to that of Norway during the last ice age.

As yet we have only a superficial knowledge of the climate in the interior of the North Polar Basin, and even that is based on comparatively few observations. In the past it has generally been assumed that the temperatures and wind velocities are fairly moderate in the central Polar Sea, and never reach the extreme values recorded in some of the arctic land areas bordering it. No wind velocities greater than thirty-five miles per hour were observed during the *Fram* and *Maud* expeditions. The lowest temperature recorded on the *Fram* expedition was −62° F., and −46° F. on the *Maud* expedition. However, this assumption may be wrong, as we found during our ice island expedition. Furthermore, Peary encountered temperatures as low as −66° F. on his march toward the Pole in 1906, and had wind velocities of gale force on several occasions. The Russians on the ice floe frequently spoke of storms and blizzards exceeding sixty miles per hour.

During the last decade the arctic regions have warmed up noticeably. This is shown by the rise of average temperatures, the distribution of the pack ice and the recession of the glaciers in Norway, Spitsbergen and Greenland. According to Ahlmann the average thickness of the polar pack ice has decreased 40 per cent during the forty-five years between the *Fram* and *Sedov* expeditions, and one glacier in Northwest Greenland has receded almost four hundred feet in thirteen years. If these conditions were to continue, the well-known glacier Svartisen in northern Norway would completely disappear in less than a hundred years. Some meteorologists, however, believe that this change of climate has now come to at least a temporary standstill.

When one compares the most extreme conditions as judged by the mean temperature of the coldest month, arctic Alaska comes off fairly well, with an average temperature of —20° F., as against —35° F. in the northern part of arctic Canada, and a probable average of at least —30° F. for the greater part of the Polar Basin.

A feature of great importance to man in the Arctic is the vertical temperature distribution in the lower air layers. In clear weather the snow-covered areas cool off markedly. When there is no wind the coldest spot is actually on the surface of the snow; and only a few feet from the surface either way—down or up— it may be measurably warmer.

It is obvious that the success of any human enterprise in the North Polar regions depends greatly on the weather. The steady increase of activity in these areas has made it important for us to know more about precisely how the weather affects man's chances to survive there. This was one of the main reasons for the T-3 expedition.

During late fall and winter activity is greatly hampered by frequent storms, with drifting snow, and by the short hours of daylight or twilight. In the central Polar Basin there are several months of almost complete darkness, when the only sources of natural light are the moon and the aurora borealis.

In general, early spring is the most attractive season for human existence in the Polar Basin, and has always been the period of greatest activity—the time when the long journeys were preferably made. During these weeks the sun may shine continuously day after day from a clear blue sky with such intensity that in Greenland I was often able to hunt seal and drive my dogs sitting on the sledge in my shirt sleeves, although the temperature was below zero.

In the course of April or May the temperature increases rapidly, and cloud formations produce a heavy low overcast which may persist for weeks at a time. Life then is a monotonous existence in a dull gray light without shadows or contrast, under the same unbroken layers of clouds day after day.

Close to the land the melting may begin early in May, increasing rapidly in the course of June and July. Living on the pack ice then becomes most uncomfortable. The cold is no longer a problem, but the thaw is, and may be even more difficult to combat. Water pours everywhere from the melting snow. The air is saturated with moisture and everything becomes damp. Often I have waded through slush up to my knees soaked through to the skin all day, and at night gone to sleep in a moist sleeping bag. The drying of clothes and gear becomes a major problem.

Finally the melting snow and open leads make any advance over the drift ice practically impossible. Hummocks, which in winter are partly smoothed by drifted snow, are in summer exposed as a chaotic jumble of irregular masses of ice, surrounded by melting snow and slush ice in which the traveler may sink to his waistline. His advance may be blocked by fresh-water pools concealed by new-fallen snow, or new ice too thin to carry his weight. Wide-open leads may force him to make long detours or resort to the use of a boat.

From the air all these obstacles may be obscured, for in the peculiar gray light of the arctic summer there are no contrasting shadows to bring out the unevenness of the ice in the North Polar Basin.

CHAPTER FOUR

Ice

Ice is the predominant feature of the geography of the polar regions. From the interior of the arctic lands, the ice caps that lie between nunataks and mountains send out glacial arms which slope down toward the tundra and in some places extend all the way to the ice-covered Polar Sea. The transition from snow-bound land to ice-bound sea may be so unnoticeable that the coastline can hardly be distinguished at first sight. Beyond the rim of the arctic coasts the ice cover is, for all practical purposes, one compact impenetrable body—a "trackless, colorless, inhospitable desert of ice"—consisting of countless masses of floating ice floes in a state of utmost confusion, constantly broken up and formed anew, moving in a slow, sluggish manner in a general clockwise direction from Alaska and Siberia toward Greenland.

The action of wind and tide breaks the frozen surface of the sea, and the sheets, yielding to the pressure, collide, slide over or under one another, and build up into hummocks thirty feet high or more. These mountains of ice drift about in the Polar Basin, and may eventually be carried into the Atlantic Ocean with the East Greenland Current to melt in the warmer sea at lower latitudes.

The sea ice, which covers 17 per cent of the surface of our globe, plays such a significant role in nature and in the life of mankind that it warrants a closer study. We find ice on all continents, on all oceans and in the atmosphere. Not only does it cover the soil in the glaciated areas of the Arctic, but it also penetrates deep into the ground as permafrost in regions where the mean annual temperature near the surface is below zero degrees centigrade. This means that permafrost underlies one-fifth of the land surface of the world, in some places going deeper than five hundred feet. In Alaska it often presents serious problems in building construction.

Ice is always being formed and melting away, alternately growing and shrinking. It is the key to a multitude of mechanical, physical and morphological phenomena; it is the direct or indirect cause of never-ending changes in the mountains, in the water and in the atmosphere. One cannot, therefore, write of the ice on our earth without mentioning the phenomena related to it.

The sea ice forms on the surface of water throughout the North Polar Basin, and depends for its existence on the fact that, during most of the year, it loses a great deal more heat by radiation to the atmosphere than it gains from the sun. Once it has attained a certain thickness in the middle of winter, it changes very little until the end of May. When it begins to melt in June and July, it melts more under the influence of radiation (i.e., the heat transmitted through the rays of the sun) than under the influence of the air temperature, which under high latitudes rises only slightly above the freezing point.

The sea ice passes through a regular annual cycle. During the brief summer melting season, it loses an average of about three feet off the top. During the winter, it increases in thickness by freezing on the bottom.

The freezing up of the open polar seas is a gradual process. In the fall, when the sea has been quite still for some days, the surface of the water begins to solidify, and takes on a greasy appearance as the first indication of freezing. Then, when the water has cooled to about 28.6° F., small ice crystals form and almost become visible. These crystals have the shape of columns and small plates grouped in bundles, and at first can hardly be distinguished. Soon, however, they grow and attain a length of more than an inch, and increase until the water is covered with a mush of crystals: this is the slush ice. It glues together like a porridge, and may be over a foot thick. Then lumps of ice form in the porridge, growing in size, solidifying and eventually cementing together to form irregular fields. If undisturbed, the whole surface freezes over, and the ice cover spreads across the water and increases rapidly in thickness: the young ice has been formed.

Newly formed ice grows rapidly and may attain a thickness of four to five inches in the first forty-eight hours. From then on the growth is slower. On the bay by our trappers' cabin on Clavering Island, Greenland, at a temperature of −40°F., I have seen the ice layer grow to a thickness of one inch in half an hour, a foot in two days, and about three feet in two weeks. However, even in the center of the North Polar Basin, a new layer seldom becomes more than six feet or at the most nine feet thick in the course of one year. The reason for this is that ice, being a very poor conductor of heat, protects the surface of the water beneath it from rapid cooling; and the protective effect increases with the growth of the ice. Over a period of years the ice may reach a thickness of fifteen feet or more. In the antarctic regions a year's growth of ice is only half that of the arctic, because there the accumulated snow, which is an even worse conductor of heat than ice, greatly retards the rate of ice formation. In the Polar Basin's pack ice the snow cover is very small, often only a few inches deep.

With the motion of the sea, cracks and leads break open in the young ice. These widen and close with the action of swell, waves and tide, and new ice forms in the open leads. Under the influence of wind and waves the thin and fragile ice fields break up and are shattered into pieces, crushed and splintered. The fragments twist and turn and are shaped into round pancakes, which freeze together and fuse into a chaos of ice, only to be broken up again. A strong movement of the ice heaps the fragments up into hummocks. Water splashed on the ice, together with falling snow, cements the pieces into an uneven, complex and confused, solid and chaotic mass: the pack ice.

In this mass new fissures are constantly forming, some straight, others running criss-cross, and widen into channels or leads of continually varying widths, separating the large ice fields or ice floes.

In the course of the winter the gradually thickening ice becomes more solid and more rigid and eventually covers the sea like a sheet of armor. Though now offering more resistance, it still yields to the force of tide, currents and wind. Under this terrific pressure the pieces of ice grind together, clash, crush, break apart. Water from the leads splashes across the ice, only to freeze at once and glue the edges together.

At the fringes of the polar pack ice the ice rises and sinks with the swell, scatters or is pressed together by the action of the wind, until it slowly melts in the warmer waters.

Along the arctic coast the ice shell rises on the tide, forming tidal cracks along the shore ice. With the turning tide the sea level is lowered and some of the ice may separate and hang up between the shores of the bays and narrow straits, only to give way to the pressure of the next rising tide. And so it goes on throughout the arctic winter.

With the return of the arctic spring and the rising sun the

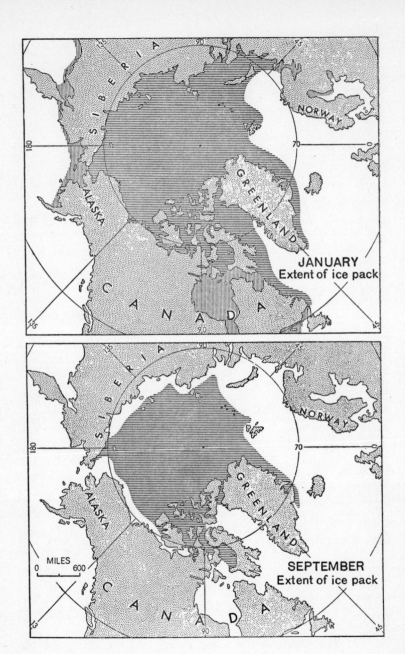

JANUARY
Extent of ice pack

SEPTEMBER
Extent of ice pack

thaw begins. The snow on the ice melts, forming streams of running water, pools and lakes. The floes become detached, scatter and float away in the open areas created by the currents and wind, drifting farther apart not to unite again that summer. The ice grows soft and fragile and is crushed by the restless sea; caves are hollowed out so that the floes disintegrate easily under wave action. Thus the ice gradually dwindles. In the center of the Polar Basin, however, the greater part of the ice survives the summer and grows anew as freezing sets in in the fall.

As a rule the ice melts more rapidly near the coasts, where the water from the land and rivers carries continuous supplies of heat into the sea, and where the atmosphere has been warmed by the dark surface of the land, which absorbs much heat during the arctic summer. Attacked also by the mechanical action of water from below, the ice foot along the arctic shores breaks and melts, forming open water between the ice field and the shore. This marginal lane is of great importance for navigation, for it is here that ships can penetrate into the pack ice earliest in the season.

The polar ice is always an impressive spectacle, whether in the gray polar mist or in the sparkling sunshine of the arctic summer, and one's first sight of it is a never-to-be-forgotten experience. I clearly recall my initial acquaintance with it when we sailed to the west from Spitsbergen in July, 1939. For days on end we plowed through the broad belt of pack ice sweeping down from the Polar Basin along the coast of Greenland to the Atlantic. At nightfall the midnight sun hung like a copper disc in the western sky, shedding a purple light over the snow-clad ice, which flashed back the light in all the colors of the rainbow. Drifting ice floes and bergs were reflected in the

shining green water, and enveloping all was that eternal still-
ness of the Arctic, occasionally broken by the roar of the heavy
ice against the side of the ship.

The pack ice, moving at a speed of ten miles a day, is carried
southward by the strong current that sweeps along the entire
east coast of Greenland, forming an ice belt that is anywhere
from twenty to three hundred miles across, its width varying
from season to season and from year to year. Sometimes it
completely envelops Jan Mayen Island and reaches even to the
northwest shore of Iceland, completely blocking the entire
space between Greenland and Iceland. At Cape Farewell, the
southeast tip of Greenland, it turns west and surges northward
through Davis Strait along the west coast of Greenland, or is
carried into the Atlantic where it melts.

The saltier sea water is, the lower the temperature at which it
freezes. Normal sea water of 35 ^{0}/$_{00}$ (per mille) salinity freezes at
28.6° F., but it can be cooled considerably below that point
without freezing when no ice or snow comes in contact with it.
When snowflakes fall into water which is already close to freezing, they hasten the process both by cooling the water and by
forming nuclei around which ice crystals develop.

The ice crystals formed during the initial stage of freezing
are of pure ice, as the pure molecules of water, without salt,
are the first to freeze. The salt remains in the water between
the crystals of ice, which eventually grow together. In the
process the dissolved salts are liberated and given off to the
unfrozen water beneath. During continual periods of hard frost,
however, the salt may appear as crystals on the surface. These
crystals are well known to arctic travelers and are referred to
by the Siberian name of *rassol.* Water splashed across the ice
during storms may leave a layer of salty slush on its surface.

Newly formed sea ice usually contains 5 to 15 per mille salt. For this reason it is not suitable as a source of drinking water. However, salt-water ice thaws more readily than fresh-water ice, and in time the salt element is excluded through a process of melting and refreezing. This process is greatly accelerated in the hummocks.

Thus, the supply of fresh-water ice for drinking purposes in the North Polar Basin does not present such a difficult problem as many people may expect. From May to September there are usually ample accumulations of fresh melt water on the ice. For centuries the Eskimos hunting on the sea ice have produced their drinking water by melting snow in bags of walrus intestines carried underneath their parkas. In this way, utilizing surplus body heat which would have been more or less wasted otherwise, they obtain all the fresh water they need.

This method I have tried successfully myself. Once in Alaska I got a quart of water in five hours by melting snow in two rubber bags which I kept inside my parka during a six-mile march and subsequent camp activities. The amount of heat required was insignificant compared with the total metabolism of the body. Otherwise, neither in the Polar Basin nor off the coast of Greenland have I ever experienced any serious difficulty in obtaining an ample quantity of drinking water—in the summer from fresh-water pools on the ice, and in winter by melting ice from the tops of hummocks.

Sometimes one may find gravel, clay, pieces of driftwood or shells on the polar drift ice. This phenomenon has been explained by Sverdrup in the following way: Every winter ice floes run aground along the shallow coasts of Alaska and Siberia, and gravel, clay, shells and stones freeze to the lower surface. The following summer the upper surface of the floe melts. The floe becomes dislodged and may drift off from the coast. During winter new ice forms below the layer of gravel and clay, and with the extensive melting of the upper surface the following summer the gravel layer appears to have moved upward. Eventually, at the end of two or three years the gravel, clay and stones become visible on the surface of the floe. These solid particles now accelerate the melting to such an extent that holes develop in the floes. Some of the gravel sinks to the bottom of the sea, far from its place of origin, for the pack ice, as we know, is in a state of constant drift.

CHAPTER FIVE

The Biology of the Polar Basin

D uring our flight to T-3, I looked down on the white infinite desert of ice that covers the Polar Basin, hoping to catch a glimpse of a diving seal at the edge of an open lead. I was not surprised that I didn't see one, for the biology of the Polar Basin is peculiar. The almost continuous sheet of ice that covers the Basin throughout the year absorbs so much light that even during the arctic summer the development of plant life in the underlying water is discouraged. To make conditions still worse, the temperature of the sea water approaches the freezing point.

It is true that in the open leads which receive the summer daylight conditions are more favorable. However, as a rule the leads do not last very long. Furthermore, during a great part of the summer they are covered with a layer of nearly fresh water produced by the surface melting of the ice, which evidently has a retarding influence on the development of marine plant life. Another adverse circumstance was discovered when Nansen reported that diatoms* found in profusion in the autumn near the surface of the more or less open sea northwest of the New Siberian Islands had by October become frozen into the ice in such quantities as to give it a brownish color.

As a result of these various circumstances one finds very

* Microscopic unicellular algae.

little plant life in the interior of the Polar Sea, which in turn is the cause of the extreme scarcity of animal life. While there may be a great variety of species, particularly of crustacea, there is as a rule only a relatively small number of individuals.

To illustrate the utter poverty of plankton life in the Polar Sea, Nansen mentions that by letting the tow net hang in the water for days or weeks while the ship drifted with the ice, they would collect no more plankton organisms than might be taken in the summer by a single vertical haul through a few fathoms of water in the Norwegian Sea.

On the other hand, during the summer, when the water of the polar currents divests itself of its ice covering and meets the warmer water from the south, there is a sudden and tremendous development of marine life. Then plant life teems in the surface waters in such profusion that the sea assumes a greenish brown color. Thus one finds the greatest fisheries in the world where polar water and Atlantic water meet—for example at the fishing banks off Iceland, West Greenland, Newfoundland and at the Lofoten Islands off the Norwegian coast. To these regions swarms of seals migrate along the margins of the drifting pack ice in Denmark Strait, off Newfoundland and Jan Mayen and in the White Sea. It was also in these regions that the Greenland whales gathered in large numbers before they were exterminated.

Nansen has explained this phenomenon in the following way: Since the thick ice covering of the Polar Basin prevents the full development of plant life, the nutritive constituents containing nitrogen and phosphorus, etc., which are brought to the top by diffusion are stored and accumulated in the surface layer of water. When the water reaches the more southern latitudes, the melting of the ice cover permits light to penetrate and chlorophyll is formed. Simultaneously, the temperature of the water increases, greatly facilitating the assimilation of these substances by the organic life which flourishes under the more favorable conditions there. In short, the Polar Basin serves as a depot for vital substances which form the basis for the abundance of marine plant life in more temperate zones.

All this has a direct bearing on the biology of the Polar Basin, a subject of much dispute among explorers and arctic travelers to whom the possibilities for survival on the pack ice are of vital concern. Mainly, the question has been whether or not one may expect to find a sufficient number of seal to enable an experienced hunter to live "off the land."

The extremes of opinion have been represented by such eminent authorities as Vilhjalmur Stefansson and Roald Amundsen. Stefansson states that "on the basis of our present knowledge the presumption of seals in every part of the Arctic Sea is so strong that it is no more than a justifiable risk to undertake crossing that entire sea afoot with sledges, living by hunting."

In contrast to this Amundsen writes: "A more unreasonable distortion of conditions in the North has never been set forth than that a skillful marksman can 'live off the land.' Stefansson has never done it, in spite of the fact that he says he has. I am willing to stake my reputation as a polar explorer, and will wager everything I own, that if Stefansson were to try it he would be dead within eight days, counting from the day of starting, if only this experiment takes place on the polar ice, which is constantly adrift over the open sea."

It might be justified to suggest that both authorities may be going too far to prove their point. In any case man has been known to starve for as long as ten weeks and still survive.

During the drift of the *Fram*, Nansen came to the conclusion

that there are few seals in the central Polar Basin, his explana-
tion being the absence of sufficient food, for reasons already
described.

Stefansson, on the basis of his experience along the north coast
of Alaska and in the Beaufort Sea, maintains that Nansen is
in error and was basing his conclusions on too limited observations. Stefansson points out that he and his companion, Storkerson, were able to live on seal which they killed in the Beaufort
Sea during the spring and the summer. However, this does not
mean that the same achievement would be possible in the
central Polar Basin. Furthermore, Stefansson and his companion
were highly skilled hunters, unusually experienced in the difficult art of killing seals on the ice.

Sverdrup's observations during the two-year drift of the
Maud led him to conclude that there is little animal life in the
drift ice in the shallow waters north of Siberia. In particular
there are few seals, and fewer the farther one moves from the
coast. He is in complete agreement with Nansen, maintaining
that in these regions one cannot expect to subsist by hunting,
except possibly during March and April when conditions for
hunting seal and walrus are favorable. During the two-year
period, according to Sverdrup's records, they saw a total of 80
seals, of which they succeeded in obtaining 18, 34 bears, of
which they secured 19, and approximately 125 walrus, of which
they killed 10. It should be noted that these observations refer
to an area which is fairly close to land, between 70° N. and
76° N.

Amundsen and his companions saw one seal (*Erignathus barbatus*) in the open lead where they landed in May, 1925, at
88° N., but observed no other mammal life during the twenty-
five days they remained on the ice.

Papanin and his group report having seen five sea gulls and two snow buntings at 88° N., a female polar bear with two cubs at 87° 53′ N., and at least one seal at 88° 01′ N., after three months' drift on the ice floe. Apparently no mammal life was encountered north of 88° N.

In my own experience I have found it hard enough at times to secure sufficient supplies of fresh food even while traveling along the arctic coast, for the occurrence of game may vary greatly from season to season and from year to year, even in the same locality. In East Greenland I once hunted for days during the late fall without coming across a single seal, though they had been abundant in the same fjord only a few weeks earlier. Similarly we expected to find a large number of seals when we arrived at Independence Fjord, North Greenland, in 1947, for earlier expeditions had reported that they were particularly plentiful in that locality. However, we saw only one during our entire stay of three weeks. On this occasion it was no cause for concern, for there were plenty of musk oxen. As far as the actual Polar Basin is concerned, I have seen numbers of seals as much as thirty or forty miles north of Alaska but no sign of one during my many low-level flights across the interior of the Basin. I would therefore be very reluctant to stake my life on the hope of living by hunting only, at least in the central Polar Basin.

These observations represent about all the factual knowledge we possessed on the occurrence of animal life in the Polar Basin at the time when we were planning the expedition to the ice island in the spring of 1952. On these facts we had to base our prospects of living "off the land" in case of emergency.

It would be safe to say that the seal is the principal animal of the Arctic because of its wide distribution, its abundance

and its role in the life of the arctic people. In the old Eskimo
community the seal, and especially the ringed seal, was the
very basis of existence, yielding everything necessary to maintain
life, and Eskimo migration was to a great extent governed by
their occurrence, supply and habits. From the seal meat the
Eskimo obtained his "daily bread," from the pelt he made his
clothing, and from the seal blubber he got his fuel for cooking
and heating.

The Eskimos eat every part of the ringed seal, except the
skin and the bones. From a nutritional point of view the internal
organs have the greatest value, because of their rich vitamin
content. It is therefore extremely interesting that the Eskimos
regard the entrails as a particular delicacy. Like the primitive
people they are, they have known how to exploit the phenomena
of nature to the utmost, and nutritional diseases used to be unknown among them, owing to the effective way in which they
utilized the products of their country.

While there are altogether six types of seal in the Greenland
waters, there appear to be only two species in the Polar Basin:
the ringed seal (*Phoca foetida*) and the bearded seal (*Erignathus
barbatus*), the ringed seal being by far the more common variety.

The ringed seal usually live close to the land where the ice
breaks up first in the spring and where they can find an abundance
of food: polar cod, herring and crustacea. All winter they maintain small openings in the fjord ice or the land-fast ice—
breathing holes—where they can come up from time to time
for a "breath of fresh air" between dives. Each seal may have
a series of four or five holes, about a mile apart. Here the
Eskimo stands ready with his harpoon. Many a time I have
watched a hunter stand for hours almost motionless at the edge
of a breathing hole, waiting to catch the seal the moment its
body shot up out of the water.

I remember one day in the fall, many years ago, when I discovered seal tracks on the innermost shore of a fjord in Northeast Greenland. A ringed seal had come out of the ice, but its hole had frozen over in the meantime and it had not been able to find any place to go down. Back and forth and up and down the fjord it had wandered in hopes of finding an opening. The trail went all the way to our cabin, and there the poor animal lay with its flippers half worn off from the floundering struggle through the snow.

When the spring sun begins to melt the ice, the seal likes to lie along the cracks or beside a hole to take a nap in the sunshine. On days like this it is loath to go back into the water and it may be possible to drive it up within reach of the dogs. Otherwise it is necessary to proceed with extreme caution; usually we had to rig up a white sail in the Eskimo manner and push it in front on a sled, while crawling along the ice on our bellies. This kind of hunting is both exciting and interesting, though the final result is usually holes in the trousers and no seal. One has to bide one's time, for the bullet must be planted in the center of the seal's skull, and that is no large target.

Seal hunting in the fall is quite a different matter. At this time of the year the seal is fat, and floats, so that it can be shot in the water. The hunter exploits its natural curiosity and tries to entice it over to the edge of the ice or to the boat with all kinds of cunning tricks. The method varies with the individual. I have seen Eskimos lying near the edge of the ice, scratching the ice and moving their feet in the air the way the seal moves his hind flippers. Some trappers sing melancholy love songs or rattle the oars, with good results. In the dark evenings in the fall we used to light a lantern in the boat; the seal would come toward the light and fall an easy victim to our large-calibered blunderbuss. Very often, however, it made fools of us. It knew enough to keep a respectful distance, popping up and vanishing suddenly like a ghost in the night. Sometimes we sat by the hour with a finger on the trigger. The finger often turned both white and blue before anything happened. It required patience and a certain sense of humor.

In the areas where seal are abundant one may see their black heads appearing above the water in rapid succession as soon as an open lead has formed. Along the arctic coast the Eskimos prefer to hunt the seal in the leads close to the shore; very seldom do they cross the leads which separate the land-fast ice from the drift ice, for fear of being carried away. Day after day they drive out on the ice with a skin boat on a sledge, perhaps waiting for hours near a lead for a seal to appear within shooting range. Sometimes they harpoon it to prevent it from sinking, or paddle out in a kajak to bring it in to the ice.

I have also watched Eskimos catch seals with a net along the open leads or through the ice. A hole is made in the ice with four smaller holes around it. The net is lowered through the central hole, and the four corners are stretched out beneath the ice with the aid of long hooks inserted in the smaller holes. When the seal comes up to breathe, it becomes entangled in the net as it struggles to dive. At times one man may catch forty seals this way in a single night.

In the early spring the females gather on the ice to breed, or give birth to the young on a shelf in the ice underneath the snow close to the breathing hole. During the first few weeks of its life the young seal is helpless and depends entirely on its mother for survival. As soon as they are capable of caring for themselves, the young generally migrate to the coast and stay near the edge of the shore ice where there are usually open leads. When mature at the age of three or four years they return to the fjords, where they often remain for the rest of their lives.

A seal may climb up on the ice to sleep or it may take a nap in the water, lying motionless, floating on the surface with its flippers close to its sides and its head submerged so that only its back is above water. In this position it sometimes remains several minutes without moving. Then as if by reflex, and apparently without awakening, it raises its head until its snout is above the water, opens its nostrils, and takes several breaths in rapid succession. Then the nostrils close again and the head sinks in the sea while the seal continues to sleep. At the end of another few minutes the same series of actions is repeated. Once in a while, it opens its eyes for a few seconds just as it is about to submerge to see if there are any enemies about. Then the eyes slowly close and the head sinks back into the water.

In distribution and habits the ringed seal has much in common with the bearded seal, which takes its name from the conspicuous tufts of coarse bristles jutting from its muzzle. However, the bearded seal is much larger, attaining a length of nine to ten feet, and is more inclined to take advantage of open leads and natural access to open water than to maintaining breathing holes throughout the winter. It is somewhat solitary in habit, although herds of bearded seals may be seen in the mating season. To the Eskimos the meat of the bearded seal is particularly palatable, and its smooth hide makes the best soles for their boots—the ugruk mukluks.

Wherever seals congregate on the pack ice, the polar bear is there to hunt. This huge yellow-white nomad is without challenge the monarch of the arctic land mammals, whether one beholds him on his constant wanderings along the edge of the ice, or on his cunning hunting trails after seal in the water, or on the way to and from his winter lair in the valleys.

The old bear hunters claim that his proper home is in East Spitsbergen and King Charles Island, where he apparently prefers to hibernate. During the greater part of the year he is constantly on the move, waddling along the edge of the ice, where he catches seal in the open water. One of his main routes runs from King Charles Island and Spitsbergen to Greenland and back again.

The bear follows the light; in the fall he comes southward, and in the spring he heads north again to his "kingdom of the midnight sun." He stays mainly in the ice belts along the arctic coasts and gathers where the seals are most plentiful. Once in a while he may wander away into the central Polar Basin, where he has been seen as far north as 88° N.; or he may be carried away to the south on scattered ice floes, and land on remote islands or coasts where he may roam around for a considerable time. This happened once on St. Lawrence Island in Bering Strait, where a bear remained for a whole year. If necessary he can swim hundreds of miles in open water, and can move so fast in the sea that a man in a rowboat has trouble catching up with him. Recently one of my companions on the T-3 expedition observed a bear with two cubs in open water one hundred miles north of Alaska. They were swimming northward toward the edge of the pack ice, which at that particular time was another hundred miles farther north.

The polar bear has a circumpolar distribution. His migrations are influenced by the availability of food, and to some extent by the movement of the ice. Some authorities speak of a circumpolar migration from the regions of Franz Josef Land and Spitsbergen south along Greenland, west and north through the

Canadian Arctic Archipelago, through the Beaufort Sea north of Alaska, and along the northern rim of Siberia back to Spitsbergen.

This regal giant weighs not far from a ton, but he has the suppleness of a tiger. He roams around in solitude, except during the mating season in the spring. Then I have seen as many as half a dozen bears in one small area of the drift ice.

The bear has a technique of his own in catching seals. Seeking cover behind the hummocks in the pack ice, he sneaks up on the seal as it sleeps lazily in the sunshine. With incredible patience he advances yard by yard, throws himself suddenly forward and crushes the seal's skull with a well-directed single blow. Often, I have watched him from a distance as he crawled toward his victim. Once, on a warm spring day, I saw him approach a bearded seal sleeping on the edge of a level drifting ice floe. He stood motionless for a long time, as though he were planning his attack. Silently he glided out into the water, swam underneath the surface toward the seal, paddling gracefully with his front limbs, his hind legs trailing behind as a rudder. Occasionally he raised his head to keep an eye on his prey, covering the black spot at the tip of his nose with his left front paw. Close to the edge of the ice he suddenly shot up from the water and launched a violent blow at the seal with his right front paw. He missed, and the seal slid into the water between his feet. The furry giant leaped up onto the floe and in his fury began to toss lumps of ice about.

Sometimes a bear will eat almost an entire seal at once; or he may save part of it for a later occasion. The polar bear eats everything. To be sure, he prefers seal blubber, but when he is hungry he does not scorn even rope ends, empty crates or human beings. After a heavy meal of seal meat and blubber he often makes for land to feed on edible roots and other vegetable foods. Occasionally during the summer season he captures eider ducks in the sea by paddling slowly in among the flock with only his head, like a piece of floating ice, above the water. If the birds try to escape by diving, the bear, plunging like an otter, makes his capture below the surface.

At times the polar bear can be very comical. Once we saw a fully grown bear sitting in the snow in a narrow fjord in Northeast Greenland trying to catch low-flying snow buntings with his front paws. As the birds dove by, he would clap his paws together, and look very disappointed when he opened them and discovered that they were empty.

He is among the most curious of animals. Any suspicious object he must investigate. As he slowly strides along he often pauses and sits down, pointing his nose up in the air to smell better. If he finds anything in his way, he eliminates it with a couple of blows. To attract his attention the trappers often burn blubber, which he can smell miles away. A string with a couple of rattles on one end is tied to a piece of blubber or seal meat which is left outside the cabin. When the bear comes along, and removes the bait, the noise of the rattles warns the trapper, who fires at him through a small hole in the cabin door.

Apparently only the pregnant females burrow, although the male polar bears occasionally seek shelter in a lair in the snow during periods of bad weather. The expectant female bear digs a burrow deep in the drifted snow among the jumble of shore ice on the coast. The main cave is separated from the entrance tunnel by an elevated doorstep, and the opening is soon closed by drifting snow. The cubs, often twins, arrive late in the winter, probably during January or February. They are very small, the size of a fully grown rat, almost naked, and blind, and are usually kept in the sheltered lair until March.

The female polar bear is a devoted mother, constantly guarding the woolly cubs, sheltering them during blizzards, ferrying them across open lanes in the drift ice, and teaching them with great patience the art of stalking seals. The cubs suckle the mother approximately one year, and remain with her during the first two years of their life.

The bear mother is often seen walking with a cub or two between her front and hind legs. It is unwise to disturb such a family unless your rifle is reliable, for a female bear with cubs can be quite aggressive and is respected even by the Eskimos. In the early days the trappers often caught bears by putting strychnine inside a lump of blubber which was left on the ice attached to a large pole. If the mother was suspicious she would push the cubs aside and inspect the food for herself, and if she was satisfied she usually shared it equally with the young ones.

Generally speaking the bear avoids man, and if he observes a dog team on the ice he usually wastes no time in taking to his feet. In hunting the bear, both Eskimos and white hunters often use specially trained dogs. Overtaking the bear, the dog bites him in the hind legs: the bear, annoyed, turns around to strike, but the dog is much quicker, jumps aside and bites him again in his hindquarters. This performance usually continues until the hunter gets within shooting range and kills the bear. Sometimes, however, the dog is the loser. In Northeast Greenland one fall I ran into a bear while I was traveling with dog team on the new ice. I released my leader dog, who immediately took off after the fleeing bear. As I struggled to keep the rest of the dogs under control the leader caught up with the bear and began to tackle him. Suddenly I heard a yell from the dog, and as I looked up I saw him flip way up into the air and land on the ice with his belly ripped open by the bear's claws.

By the time I reached the scene of the battle the dog was dead and the bear had escaped across some thin ice where I was unable to pursue him.

If a bear is wounded he can be quite aggressive, and during midwinter he is extremely hard to detect, for he moves along without noise. Once one of my companions, a trapper, was trailed by a big husky bear in December. He was carrying a log of driftwood on his shoulder and suddenly the bear pounced from behind and hit the log. They were both a bit confused, but the man was the first to recover. He cocked his rifle and fired without aiming as the bear was about to charge. He missed, and as he started to run he cocked his rifle again, but the cartridge stuck. The bear, momentarily bewildered by the shot, recovered and came after him. The man got down behind a large block of ice by the shore, and tried to remove the cartridge with the aid of a knife. Then the bear appeared on top of the ice block. Losing no time, my friend grasped the gun by the barrel and struck the bear on the head with the butt, took to his feet and reached the cabin safely. The bear apparently had had enough, for he remained by the ice block, where he was later shot by the trapper with another rifle.

Many an old-timer has claimed that a polar bear will not harm a man who is standing still, but will invariably pursue and attack if he attempts to run away. Once an unarmed sailor was surprised by a bear in Northeast Greenland. The bear stood there watching him until the sailor took to his feet. The bear followed, and the terrified sailor threw away his jacket in order to run faster. When he saw that the bear stopped to examine the jacket, he kept on throwing off his clothes. Each time a new item of clothing was discarded the bear made a halt to examine it closely. By the time the sailor reached the boat he was nude.

The bear came close and licked the sailor's hand, but fled when the rest of the party arrived.

Actually, a bear's attitude is quite unpredictable. At times he will stalk and attack a man; at other times he will flee like a ghost at the slightest scent of human beings. His sense of smell is incredibly keen, but his small dark eyes are undependable at long range, and his hearing appears to be poor.

In the wake of the polar bear the fox runs far and wide all along the coast to feed on whatever unconsumed food the bear has left behind. The fox prefers the mainland, but it is not infrequently found way out on the islands when the fjords are frozen over, or on the actual sea ice. H. U. Sverdrup saw several foxes in the pack ice during the drift of the *Maud,* and Nansen observed four fox tracks in the spring at 85° N.

This cunning little animal winters on the rocky slopes of the mountains under large flat blocks of stone, on the sunny side. On its nocturnal hunting expeditions it looks for lemming, hares, ptarmigan, and birds' eggs of every kind, or whatever edible material it may come across on its way, both to satisfy its daily needs and to provide its winter supplies. One can see it scurrying along on light paws down by the seashore in the summer, in search of sea birds and eggs, or carcasses that have washed ashore, or the fat crustaceans swarming along the beaches. The Eskimos insist that the fox can even fish by splashing with one paw on the surface of the water to attract the ignorant fish and greedy codlings.

In the summer the white fox looks very shabby, for its pelt is matted and full of blubber and all sorts of filth. But it is a sight for sore eyes to see the mother fox playing with her young in wild abandon, in the fragrant bell-heather and golden poppies, where gnats swarm by the million in the warm arctic summer sun.

Walrus have never been seen in the central North Polar Basin, but Sverdrup reports having seen large numbers in the drift ice northwest of Wrangel Island during the spring and summer. The first herds arrived in the middle of April, apparently having spent the summer close to the New Siberian Islands and east of the Taimir Peninsula, as well as north of Wrangel Island. According to the Siberian Eskimos, the walrus move to the south through Bering Strait every fall and spend the winter in the Bering Strait. In the early spring, they go north again, and large herds are encountered in July at the fringe of the drift ice in the Chuckchere Sea and along the northwest coast of Alaska.

At St. Lawrence Island in Bering Strait between Alaska and Siberia the herds of walrus appear along the coast with the first drift ice in the fall. Here they are seen in varying numbers all through the winter when there is open water along the coast. The main herds, however, arrive during March and April when several hundred are killed by the natives from their skin boats. They are clumsy giants, up to fifteen feet long and more than a ton in weight. One can watch them from the land as they rise to the surface of the sea near the edge of the ice, pull themselves out of the water with the aid of their tusks, and hump their way into the sleeping mass of bodies heaped against each other on the ice.

During the walrus season at St. Lawrence Island the old Eskimo hunters, the captains of the skin boats, gather upon the hill by the sea every morning at daybreak to watch for walrus on the drift ice. I used to join them whenever I could, for walrus hunting in the ancient Eskimo manner is an adventurous sport.

One early morning in March we discovered three large walrus on a floe a couple of miles out, and two more on a second floe further away. These were the first we had seen for many weeks, and since there was very little meat left in the village, they caused considerable excitement, even among the Eskimos. In a matter of minutes the boat crews were awakened, and while the men got their hunting gear together—rifles, harpoons, seal pokes and skin ropes—the women and children lifted the large skin boats, the umiaks, from the racks, and brought the outboard motors and the dog teams down to the beach. The dogs were brought along to pull the meat and blubber to the boat in case an animal was shot on a floe, or to pull it onto the ice in case it was shot in the water.

The rising sun shone on the high mountain by the village behind us as the old captain guided the light vessel, which surged ahead at great speed, out among the scattered floes toward the nearest group of walrus. Two more boats followed in our wake. Through the translucent walrus hide that covered the frame of the boat I could see the waves ripple along its side. In the front of the boat stood the gunner with his loaded rifle, and behind him was the harpooner. A skin rope was attached to the head of the harpoon, and the end of rope was fastened to a sealskin poke which would prevent the animal from sinking when harpooned. In the center of the boat were the dogs and the rest of the crew. The captain stood in the rear, dressed in a windbreaker made of walrus intestines.

As we zigzagged through the lanes of open water, swarms of ducks lifted from the surface and flew to the north. A tremendous flat field of ice checked our advance, but instead of making a detour, we simply pulled the boat up on the ice, and hauled it easily on its ivory runners across the floe.

The walrus were still lying at the edge of their floe as we approached across a large lane of open water. The gunner raised his rifle, and we were so close that we could see clearly their yellow-white tusks shining in the sun each time they lifted their heads. Suddenly they slipped into the water and dived before the gunner could fire. Then followed a hectic hunt after the three monsters as they dived and swam in among the scattered ice. Time and time again we would get almost within range only to see them disappear into the water. Eventually they escaped into new ice, which was too thick for the skin boat to penetrate, but too thin for a man to walk on. We could see their heads appearing here and there as they broke the ice with their strong necks each time they came up to breathe.

In the meantime the other two boats had approached the second group of walrus, and we watched them shoot one on the ice. The second animal dived but was harpooned and killed in the water.

As we returned, the entire village, including the two hundred starving dogs, gathered on the shore. After the two umiaks with the meat and blubber were beached and hauled into the village by the dog teams, the meat was shared in accordance with the tradition of the tribe, each member of the crew receiving his share and the captain the head of the animal. The rest was divided equally among the people of the village.

While walrus were once abundant in the arctic waters at high latitudes, and had a circumpolar distribution, they have gradually been exterminated and now appear in considerable numbers only along the Siberian coast, on St. Lawrence Island and at Point Hope in Alaska, a few places in the Canadian Arctic and on the northwest coast of Greenland.

They prefer shallow water not deeper than fifteen fathoms, where they feed on shellfish at the bottom of the sea. They use their tusks to dig out the mussels from the muck, and their long bristles to brush the food together in a heap on the bottom before swallowing it. Occasionally one sees pieces of marine algae that have drifted ashore where the walrus has been digging for food.

Some walrus, however, also eat seal, at least on rare occasions. This interesting fact, which is known to the old sealing captains, has been pointed out by H. U. Sverdrup, who noticed that three of the walrus which they shot on the *Maud* expedition had chunks of sealskin with blubber over ten inches long in their stomachs. He mentions that the Siberian Eskimos also knew this and had a name for seal-killing walrus. It was confirmed by information I gathered from the St. Lawrence Island Eskimos in Bering Strait. Apparently the walrus squeezes the seal to death between his front flippers and then butchers it with his tusks.

During summer and fall the walrus sometimes go up on land where there are flat sandbanks. Here they may be seen in large numbers, snoring while lazily sleeping in the sun. At such times one can walk up on the herd against the wind and get within a few yards of it. Most of their life, however, they spend riding the drifting ice floes of the northern seas. At times large herds of walrus have been seen so tightly packed in the water that the young were carried on their mothers' backs.

Of their mating and breeding habits very little is known for certain. It is probable that the mating takes place during the periods when they are gathered on land in great flocks. During the mating season the bulls fight with terrific fury, roaring and snorting as they drive their powerful tusks into the necks of their opponents.

The young are born during May or June, and are about three feet long. During the period of lactation, which lasts two years, the mothers protect their young with great care. By the end of that time the tusks are sufficiently developed to allow the young to support themselves.

As a rule, the walrus flees from human beings, but if wounded or defending the young, it can be very aggressive.

The old hands can tell amazing stories of walrus hunting in the Arctic. They used to go out in small wooden boats and attack the flocks in the water with harpoons. Sometimes they harpooned two or three animals at once from the same boat, and a deadly struggle would follow as the wounded panic-stricken animals turned on the boat with their powerful tusks or pulled it along with terrific speed in their effort to keep up with the rest of the swimming herd. Frightened and furious, the beasts would splash about in the water, snorting and whistling, charging, striking with their tusks, and diving in a roaring commotion. The foaming sea would be full of bobbing heads and ugly faces. This kind of hunting requires good nerves and a steady hand, for the only vulnerable spots are the eyes, or the nape of the neck. One usually aims at the third fold of the neck from the top. The skull is almost impenetrable.

When to this brief account of seals, polar bears, foxes and walrus I add that Nansen in 1895 saw several fairly large schools of narwhale in open leads in the pack ice close to 85° N., and that birds such as sea gulls, ducks and snow buntings occasionally may trek across the top of the world from one arctic coast to another, I have fairly well summarized our acquaintance with the animal life of the central Polar Basin. To those of us who had experienced the agony of the mosquitoes that swarm on the arctic tundra in the summer, it was a comfort to know that we could be sure of not being bothered with any insects during the T-3 expedition to the ice island near the Pole.

CHAPTER SIX

Arctic Resources

T he search for new and shorter trade routes and new resources gave early arctic exploration its greatest impetus. When the great British navigator, Martin Frobisher, set out in 1576 to find the Northwest Passage to India, he discovered new land where he came upon some "black stones," which were later thought to be gold. The fabulous tales of the "Frobisher Gold Mine," at Frobisher Bay in the eastern Canadian Arctic, created a sensation in the sixteenth century and made Elizabethan history, until the "black stones" proved worthless iron pyrites, and Frobisher's promoters went bankrupt.

The great challenges of the arctic world have tempted man to the fullest use of ingenuity and determination. Exploration in the far North has been a series of tragedies and half-won victories from the start. By virtue of the nature of the Arctic it must always be so, and although the Frobisher gold mines proved a heartbreaking failure, the spirit of Frobisher has survived and will remain the driving force in our northward expansion.

Today we know that there are vast natural resources in the circumpolar regions, essential to our progress and economic life, as well as to our military security and defense. The northward expansion of the Soviets and their development of the northern sea route reveal the important role Siberian resources play in their schemes.

The rich reserves of fish, fur, coal, timber, gold and copper in Alaska are well known and subject to energetic exploitation. Since Alaska was purchased by the United States in 1867 it has yielded almost a billion dollars in gold and other metals. Canada reaps valuable harvests from her arctic resources of coal, copper, silver, lead, uranium and nickel. The Canadian mines in the Yukon and Northwest Territories produce annually over $2 million in minerals. Port Radium at the Great Slave Lake is one of the world's greatest known sources of radioactive minerals, and there is a system of air transport to and from the mines. In Labrador there is iron; and from Spitsbergen, Norway obtains a great proportion of its coal. In the Kola Peninsula they find vanadium apatite, nickel and iron, and in the northern Urals copper, coal, oil, nickel and iron—and oil at the Taimir Peninsula. In Greenland there are cryolite and lead.

Cryolite is a rare mineral, gray-white and translucent like ice when wet. It is a fluoride of sodium and aluminum, used mainly as a flux in the Hall-Heroult process, by which practically all the world's aluminum is obtained. About 60 per cent of the purified cryolite goes to the aluminum industry, 30 per cent goes to the enamel industry, which uses cryolite for enameling hardware, and 10 per cent goes to the glass industries, where it is used in manufacturing opalescent glass.

On the southern shore of Arsuk Fjord in Southwest Greenland there is a small mining town, Ivigtut, with a total of about eighty buildings and two hundred men. It has attracted wide attention, for it is the only place on earth where genuine cryolite is found in quantities of practical importance, although there are reports of a mine in active production in East Siberia on the Manchurian border. The only two other known occurrences—at Pikes Peak, Colorado, and Miass in the Urals—are said to be small and impure.

Cryolite has been mined at Ivigtut since the middle of the last century, and is at present one of the most important assets in the Greenland economy, since all the profits go direct to the Greenland administration, which ever since Greenland became a Danish possession has been charged with the responsibility for the economy, trade, social welfare, education and medical care of the entire native population.

Up to 1939 the crude cryolite was refined in Denmark, with the exception of the quantities required in the United States and Canada (one-third of the total output) which were shipped direct to the Pennsylvania Salt Manufacturing Company in Philadelphia. It has been claimed that the Ivigtut cryolite deposits may be exhausted by 1972.

More than a hundred years ago Thomas Simpson discovered oil near Point Barrow in northern Alaska, and as early as 1904 the large plains of tundra between the Brooks Range and the arctic coast were recognized as a possible petroleum-producing territory by the United States Geodetic Survey. Preliminary surveys commenced in 1923, and the present active arctic petroleum project began in 1944, stimulated by a serious oil shortage in California during 1943.

The fact that large-scale mining operations are possible in Spitsbergen is due to the Gulf Stream which keeps the west coast, where the coal deposits are found, free from ice during a considerable part of the year. This means that coal can be shipped four and a half to five months during the summer. These coal fields, the first of which was once owned by an American, Mr. John Longyear, yielded in the year 1952 nearly 700,000 tons of coal of excellent quality, produced by a total of 3,600 men. These men earn their living under inhospitable arctic conditions, isolated, with four months of winter darkness, and temperatures of —40° F. in the winter.

The largest fishing grounds on earth are on the fringes of the arctic regions—in the waters around northern Norway, Iceland, West Greenland, Newfoundland and Alaska.

The arctic sealing industry which has been active since the early part of the last century is of considerable financial importance. More than half a million seals are killed every year from sealing vessels operating in the open sea in the three main arctic sealing fields: the White Sea, the drift ice east of Greenland, and in the waters east of Newfoundland and Labrador. The annual catch represents several million dollars in fur, skins and blubber. The Greenland seal and the hood seal form the main basis of the industry. Although the biology of these seals is not fully known, it appears that they spend the summer at the fringe of the drift ice in the far North, where food is abundant. In the late fall they move south and spend most of the winter on the fishing banks, where they gorge on fish, herring, zooplankton and other food. In the late winter they once more begin their northward migration. By the end of February they have usually reached their traditional breeding grounds, where millions of seal gather on the drifting ice and in the water. Here the young are born on the ice, and following a three weeks' lactation period, the mothers leave the cubs to mate. Then the herds move on to the north, to gather once more on the floating ice to moult. By this time the seals are in poor condition, for little or no food is consumed during the breeding and moulting season. In the course of the summer, however, they fatten up in the northern waters before the cycle begins once more.

It is the newly born seal that has the most valuable fur, the "white coat" and the "blue back," and the main seal catch therefore takes place on the breeding grounds. As the pelt of the newly born seal remains completely hair-fast only for the first eight to ten days after birth, it is essential that the sealing captains reach the main breeding fields at this time. The breeding places vary slightly from year to year, and at times the ice conditions prevent the sealing vessels from penetrating the pack.

On a sealing expedition to the Newfoundland sealing fields in 1941 we battled the ice for three months. Time and time again violent gales carried the ice and the 260-ton wooden vessel toward the coast, where the ice shattered, and the sealing captain had a hard job keeping the ship clear of the rocky cliffs.

From the crow's nest in the foremast of the boat the sealing skipper cons its way through the moving ice pack. Whenever possible he follows the open leads, winding his way in among the floes rising and sinking with the swell, constantly watching the propeller so that it will not be broken by the ice. At times the ice closes and locks the ship in a grinding grip, crushes it, heaves it up on the floes, or carries it away with the moving ice mass. In heavy ice the ship may buck and ram in vain, hitting the floes at full speed bow-on, backing only to make another run. Occasionally the crew has to dynamite a channel through the ice to open water, as they battle their way ahead toward the breeding herds.

The newly born seals are lying helplessly on the ice. Unable to swim, they fall easy victims to the sealing crew, who may kill many thousand in a single day. In the case of the Greenland seal, the old seals flee and leave the young; but the female hood seals remain with their young on the ice and defend them to the end, while the male charges the intruder with deadly fury. With inflated hood, fiery red eyes, wide-open mouth and menacing roars, he attacks viciously with his teeth. I once saw a sealer, who had broken his seal hook during the fight, being chased on an ice floe by a furious bull. He was saved by the skipper, who came to his aid with a gun.

Later in the season the sealers follow the herds of fully grown seals to the north, shooting thousands of them in the scattered ice. The gunners move on ahead, shooting the seals as they advance. If the first seals are killed instantaneously, the herds usually stay on the ice and are slaughtered by the thousands. Behind the gunners the skinning crew advances slowly, jumping from one floe to another. A practiced sealer can skin a seal in less than a minute. The pelts with the blubber are hauled across the ice and collected in a heap where they are gathered by the ship and eventually turned into products of fur, leather and oil.

Arctic sealing under these conditions is a hazardous life. The ice is in constant motion, and many of the floes are too small to support a man unless he is moving fast. It is part of the daily routine for sealers to tumble into the sea and have to swim for life in the icy slush, holding a chunk of ice under each arm for support until they can climb up onto a larger floe. It has happened that men have been caught and crushed between floes set together by the ocean swell.

Of even greater value than the hair seals of the arctic waters are the fur seals (*Callorhinus ursinus*) of the Pribilof Islands in Alaska. The herd of these extraordinary animals was discovered in 1786 by the adventurous Russian navigator, Gerasim Pribilof, who tested out an ancient Aleut legend of a group of islands far to the north of the Aleutian chain where millions of fur seals were said to migrate every year.

Since the United States purchased Alaska together with the

Pribilof Islands and their herds of fur seals from Russia in 1867, the value of the fur taken from these islands alone amounts to many times the purchase price of the entire territory of Alaska. The annual gross value of the fur catch, consisting of some seventy thousand skins, totals more than $4 million.

The present herd at the Pribilof Islands is estimated to number about 3½ million seals. Once a year these animals come to the islands to bear their young and to breed on the sandy beaches and among the rocks of the seal rookeries. The first to arrive, early in May, are the old bulls—the "beach masters." The forerunners of the great herds, these massive bulls, who are up to eight times larger than the females, fight savagely to establish themselves in the best positions on the rookery. As a rule, the largest and oldest bulls take possession of the central part of the rookery, surrounded by the younger breeding males in the periphery. From this time until the breeding season is over, a couple of months later, the breeding bull dares not leave his domain for fear that a rival may capture his harem. For almost three months he apparently neither drinks nor eats; and he sleeps very little. His life is a constant battle against aggressive competitors for the ownership of the pregnant cows that come out of the sea to breed. During this period the bull may lose as much as a quarter of his body weight; he looks like a heap of bones in a skin bag when it is all over in the fall.

During a visit to the Pribilof Islands in the breeding season in 1951 I used to sit for days at an observation post on the top of a high rock overlooking the rookery, watching the herd. As the pregnant cows clambered out of the water, the bulls would grab them and hustle them off to their harems. Some of the bulls had as many as a hundred females in their harems, others had only a single cow. The bull was constantly on guard, and every time a female attempted to escape to the neighboring harem, her master, with a roar, would grab her by the neck and toss her brutally over his head back into the group. The unfaithful female would lick the bull placatingly, and he would snort and sniff for a while before he seemed prepared to forgive the incident.

The single bulls had formed a fringe around the edge of the rookery, hoping for a chance to grab a cow to establish a harem of their own. I was watching a male who had gathered a harem upon a rock in the sea at low tide. With the rising tide his rock became submerged in the sea and his harem dissolved. At the next low tide he tried again, only to suffer the same heartbreaking disappointment as the water rose.

A few days after the arrival of the cows the young are born. Each breeding female bears only one pup a year. Within a week mating takes place, and after this the females are allowed to return to the sea to feed. Usually the mother remains at sea for about five days at a time before she comes back to the island to find her own baby among thousands of other pups. She will never nurse any but her own, so if she is killed at sea the pup will also die.

At the outskirts of the actual breeding grounds the young males come out of the water to sleep on the beach at night, and it is here that the sealers are out to kill. Early in the morning, long before daybreak, I used to accompany the Aleuts as they quietly approached the hauling ground between the sleeping animals and the sea. Suddenly they would start to shout and yell, driving the frightened animals inland a few hundred yards from the beaches, where the three-year-old males were separated by size from the rest of the herd and killed.

The seals are skinned on the killing grounds and the pelts are transported to modern plants on the islands where they are cleaned, blubbered and salted, and then shipped to the States. Here the skins are processed and tanned and turned into valuable fur coats.

During the last few generations the Arctic Sea and its islands have played an important role in the economy of the nations bordering the arctic regions. Through short-sighted and wild exploitation, as in the case of the arctic whaling industry, some of the treasures of the Arctic have finally been exhausted; at the same time new sources of valuable raw materials have been uncovered. However, in order to utilize fully the enormous resources of the vast arctic regions, man must pave his way through wild territory—over ice-bound waters, across tundras and along waterways through huge mountain ranges—carrying with him the tools and the knowledge that are the results of laborious research and technical development. In this northward expansion, where man has to settle, work and live in the remote areas of the Arctic, success or failure depends primarily on human factors.

CHAPTER SEVEN

The Human Factors

In the conquest of the polar regions man is the limiting factor. In spite of technical progress and the variety of modern mechanical equipment and gadgets available to the arctic traveler there is always a stage when the success of the entire project stands or falls with the nature of man himself. When, for instance, the snowmobile or the weasel breaks down in the middle of nowhere, without spare parts for repair, one has to rely on one's feet. Once in the interior of Alaska our weasel threw a track, and we had to walk all day and all night through the deep snow along an old abandoned trail to get back to camp.

Now we are so accustomed to the convenience of traveling by air across the vast arctic wilderness that we often fail to think of the serious consequences of mechanical failure, when a flier marooned on the ice has no one but himself to depend on for survival. In addition, under extreme arctic conditions mechanical equipment requires careful and constant attention, or it quickly becomes useless. To keep a car in operational condition at fifty or sixty below even in a town like Fairbanks is almost a full-time occupation.

While machines may be adjusted to meet the ever-changing requirements of the environment, man himself cannot change physiologically beyond certain definite limits. It is true that there are great individual differences in mental and physical resources, but the range of environmental conditions the human machine can tolerate without artificial adjustments or adequate protection is still quite narrow. Thus, while a properly winterized vehicle, once started, may run almost as well at sixty below as at above-zero weather, a man dressed to walk for any length of time at sixty below is so hampered by his bulky clothing that he soon exhausts his resources.

The arctic environment is merciless, and the records of man's northward expansion are full of recitals of its hardships and horrors—of hunger and frostbite, of the eternal darkness and monotony in ice-bound ships that caused men to lose their minds, to commit murder and suicide. Many of the tragedies of the North will remain unsolved mysteries forever. Reading these documents of human conquest, we can visualize the nightmarish marches, the exhausted humans staggering on and on, stumbling forward toward a base of safety which they never attained, leaving blood-stained tracks on the ice, and frozen companions buried in the snow behind them in the white cold world of the Arctic.

And yet, for the experienced man things as a rule go quite well in the Arctic. For those accustomed to the peculiar conditions in the polar regions, the freedom, adventure, the simple way of life, and the challenge of the elements have the greatest attraction. In fact, those who have once experienced the fascination of the arctic world have an urge to return. In my own case this longing to go back to the frozen regions somehow is strongest in the spring when the migratory birds fly north with the rising of the sun. I feel that the enjoyment of the arctic spring is worth the endurance of the agonies of the winter night.

Man's main enemy in the arctic world is the cold when it reaches the severe degrees. However, at temperatures above

—30° F. life is still fairly easy whether one is living in a town like Fairbanks or on a sledge journey across the arctic tundra. In the town, life goes on pretty much as usual with normal activities, and no one is seriously affected by the cold. People reasonably dressed move about on their business and the buses still run on schedule. In "the brush," dressed in our parkas, we bounce along on our sledges behind frisky dogs across the crisp snow sparkling in the sunlight. Once in a while we may jump off the sledge and run beside the dogs to improve our circulation. At night we pitch our tent without any trouble and sleep in comfort in our regular arctic sleeping bags.

For man, the limit for efficient outdoor operations under exposed conditions is in the vicinity of —30° F. Below —30 or —40° F. life becomes more difficult. At this point even animal activity is markedly reduced, and with increasing cold it ceases almost completely.

At temperatures such as —60° F. prolonged outdoor activities become exceedingly difficult unless one is especially equipped to combat the cold. In town the activities are reduced to a minimum; for even a visit to the neighbor becomes a problem when one has to dress as if for a North Polar expedition. Women wear slacks underneath their skirts and other multilayer garments, carrying their shoes in a bag for a change. Most cars are laid up, and those that are running are apt to rattle along on square tires and frozen shock absorbers, with the wheel so stiff from the solidified lubricants that it can hardly be turned. In cold like this a young couple driving home from a party one night almost froze to death when their engine stalled just outside the Fairbanks city limits. I also remember the occasion when the drugstore in Fairbanks caught fire in sixty below weather, and the water from the firemen's hoses froze to ice before it reached the blazing flames. On a day like that a man drove a few miles out of town in his car to take some pictures. He stopped the car to walk a short distance away from the road, and as he returned he realized that his feet were cold. The car failed to start, and by the time he finally got it going both his feet were frostbitten, and several of his toes had to be amputated. He had been wearing regular shoe packs, which are inadequate at temperatures below −20° F. The incident could probably have been avoided with the use of proper footgear.

At these extreme temperatures the experienced trapper or the arctic traveler remains in or close to his shelter. It happens occasionally, nevertheless, that even the old-timers are caught unprepared in the cold. Some of the most serious cases of frostbite I have seen were incurred by experienced trappers who were forced by lack of food to make for the nearest village during a prolonged cold spell, when the temperature was constantly below −50° F. for several weeks.

In arctic combat, as in guerilla warfare, experience has shown that the outcome depends more on the individual human soldier than it does in any other type of operation. Large-scale troop movements may be impractical; moreover, as we have learned in the past—notably in the Finnish-Russian war—large bodies of men may fall easy victims to small groups of skilled winter warriors who have learned to take advantage of the nature of the arctic environment and to make the cold their ally. In winter warfare every single degree of arctic cold is important, for those who can tolerate the greatest cold may catch and kill the enemy, helplessly trapped in his sleeping bag. This fact was amply demonstrated in the last war during the fighting in Norway, when small detachments of specially trained soldiers from my own company, dropped by parachute into the mountains in the

North, were able to tie down considerable German forces by their hit-and-run attacks on railway lines and important installations. As they withdrew to their concealed dugouts in the snow close to the Swedish border, they ambushed the pursuing Germans and left booby traps behind along their ski tracks, quickly discouraging further pursuit.

To the arctic combat flier the cold is the final opponent if he has to bail out or crash-land in the arctic no man's land.

Were it not for the numerous problems created by the cold, life in the polar regions would be fairly simple. But the cold may paralyze mechanical transportation, block the harbors, break the plumbing, freeze the water supply. Sewage disposal becomes a problem limiting human habitation. Buildings are shattered by the action of the permafrost. Cameras and other mechanical gadgets jam; the film becomes brittle and may break. Unless thoroughly cleaned of grease, firearms fail to ignite and become useless, and rubber becomes as fragile as glass. Many phases of outdoor industrial operations slow down or come to a stop. But above all the cold affects the human machine. It freezes the skin and kills the tissues, it bites in the nostrils, and freezes tears into icicles. Condensed moisture from the breath covers face and clothes with rime frost, ice glues the eyelashes together and may eventually close the eyes. It becomes dangerous to touch metal. Every minor detail of routine may become a major operation which requires extreme caution. Living becomes a hazard, for the slightest amount of carelessness may be fatal.

In recent years considerable interest has been devoted to the question of man's physiological adjustment to cold. Factors which the human being may mobilize in combating the arctic elements include "acclimatization," increased production of body heat through the elevation of metabolism, and the physiological control of heat loss, as well as the environmental protection of clothing and shelters.

While it is known that human beings can become acclimatized to heat, it is still subject to dispute whether any real physiological acclimatization to cold is possible. Here one must distinguish between the effects of "know-how," experience, "accustomization" and real physiological acclimatization.

Arctic animals adapt themselves to the changes in environment by growing a heavier pelt during winter, but man's hair is of no value in protecting him against the cold. In fact the pure Eskimo is almost devoid of hair on his body, except on the head. Nor, evidently, is the subcutaneous fat in man of significance, as it is in the seal—whose subcutaneous blubber covers its body like a thick shield and is of great importance as an insulator.

Under arctic conditions, heat, and the facilities for preparing at least one hot meal a day, in addition to hot beverages, are very important. This was clearly realized by the early arctic travelers, who solved this problem by a great variety of methods. Sixty years ago Fridtjof Nansen developed a cooking apparatus known as the Nansen cooker, which he and Johansen used during their march toward the Pole from the *Fram*. This apparatus, which was very light, enabled them to cook two hot meals a day and to melt an abundance of water over a period of 120 days, using a total of about four gallons of fuel.

Practically speaking, man will die from exposure regardless of acclimatization if he is helplessly exposed to severe cold without adequate protection against heat loss and without sufficient food to maintain his body heat. A man lying in the snow at sixty below will freeze to death in short order whether he is an Eskimo or a white.

If there is such a thing as acclimatization to cold—and several minor physiological changes in man seem to indicate such a possibility—one would expect to find it among Eskimos who are born in the Arctic, and whose forefathers have survived the arctic conditions for generations. Unquestionably, the Eskimo gets on better in the arctic environment than the whites, just as a white man gets along better than an Eskimo in New York; but this does not necessarily mean that the Eskimo is physiologically acclimatized to cold. It may just as well be a matter of racial characteristics. Furthermore, whites who are born and have spent a greater part of their lives in arctic regions are apt to feel cold just as quickly as a man from the temperate zones. With age, too, there is a tendency to feel the cold more keenly—as a distinguished scientist said: "The longer I live in Alaska, the longer and colder do the winters get."

It is surprising how well an inexperienced newcomer from the temperate zone may stand his first arctic winter, while he often may find the second winter more unpleasant. Probably many factors enter into this; in part at least it may be explained on a psychological basis: if the man is keen on his job he may be too busy to pay much attention to the cold, the new fascinating environment completely occupying his attention. On the other hand, some newcomers arrive in the Arctic with a preformed attitude of dislike and apprehension and a fear of the cold that can only lead to misery and failure.

With the first onset of the arctic winter the cold seems to be more noticeable than it is a few weeks later on, although the temperature may be dropping. This has often been taken as an indication of acclimatization. It should be remembered, however, that at the onset of winter one is usually not dressed for the cold. Later on, summer dress is exchanged for warmer clothes, and one generally takes more care in bundling up before going out. Fur-

The North Pole area from the air, showing pack ice and frozen leads.

Passing the northern extremity of the land on our way to the Pole, the northeast coast of Ellesmere Island with its sheer mountain cliffs that rose from pack ice, with ice-bound fjords, frozen rivers and valleys between the mountains.

Nunataks protruding through the ice on the mountainous coast of Greenland.

The spring thaw in Greenland.

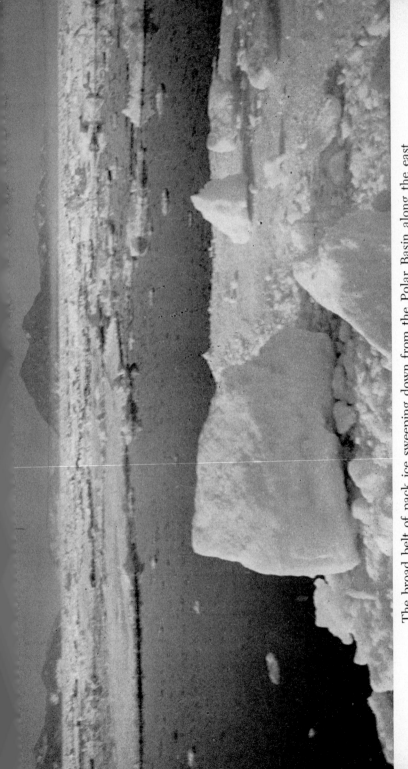

The broad belt of pack ice sweeping down from the Polar Basin along the east coast of Greenland to the Atlantic.   Photo: N. J. Rud

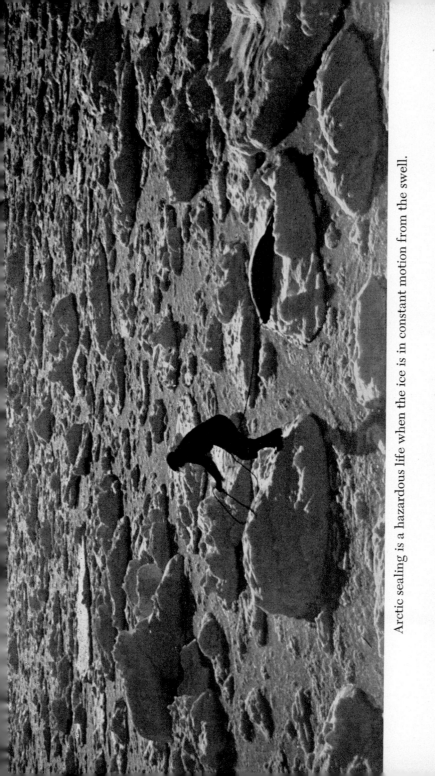

Arctic sealing is a hazardous life when the ice is in constant motion from the swell.

A young Greenland seal in the pack ice east of Newfoundland.

Walrus on an ice floe.

Young captured polar bear cubs on Myggbukta, Greenland.

Captured narwhales.

The natives of the north, the Eskimos, are easy-going people.

Eskimo boy in polar bear skin pants at Thule.

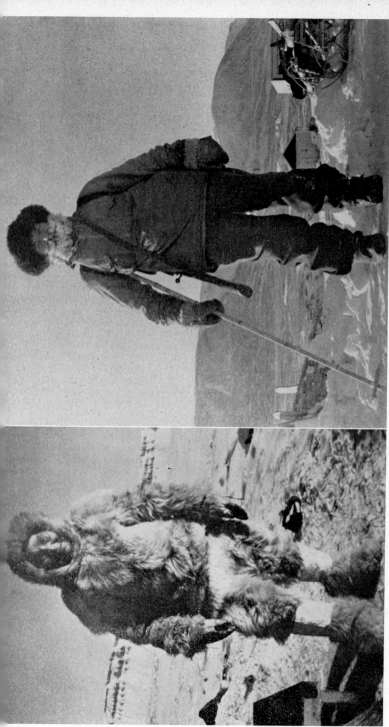

Admiral Peary's companion Ootah, the only surviving member of the party that reached the Pole in 1909.

The Norse trapper Henry Rudi, a veteran of the North, who has shot 700 polar bears.

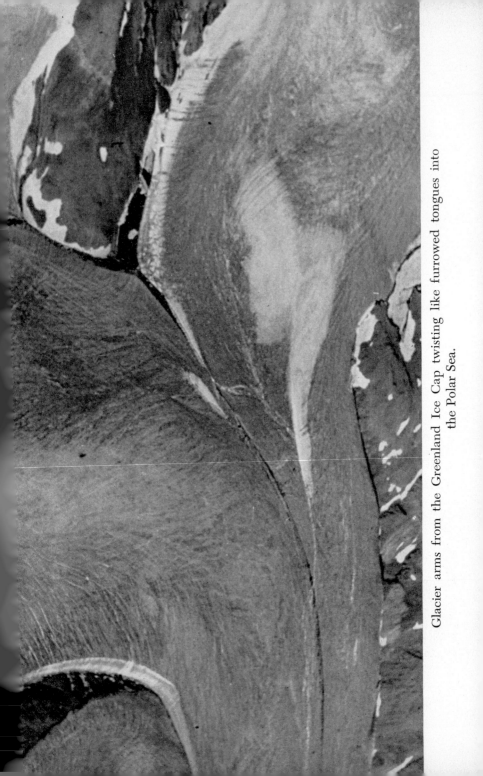

Glacier arms from the Greenland Ice Cap twisting like furrowed tongues into the Polar Sea.

The shelf ice (left) on the north coast of Ellesmere Island (right) with Ward Hunt Island surrounded by the shelf ice at the mouth of Disraeli Bay (upper right). Photo: Royal Canadian Air Force

Dog teams on the fjord
ice in East Greenland.
In the background the
edge of the inland ice.

A sealing vessel in the
heavy polar pack ice.

T-3, a floating island of ice in the center of the North Polar Basin.
Photo: U.S. Air Force

The ski-equipped C-47 after the landing on T-3.

Two views of our initial camp on T-3.   Photo: U.S. Air Force

The geophysicist Dr. Crary taking observations at the edge of the ce island T-3. Photo: Mike Brinegar

oe Fletcher making a snowhouse on T-3.

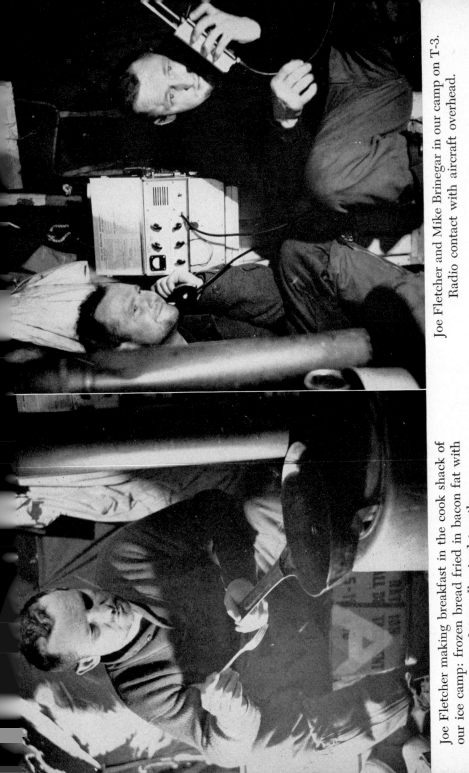

Joe Fletcher and Mike Brinegar in our camp on T-3. Radio contact with aircraft overhead.

Joe Fletcher making breakfast in the cook shack of our ice camp: frozen bread fried in bacon fat with cheese and jam all mixed together.

thermore, this phenomenon may well be the result of "accustomization," for one can get used to bathing in cold water without being physiologically acclimatized to cold.

I knew a Dutchman in Alaska, Pete Maas, who had accustomed himself to bathing in the icy river in the fall and spring, and to diving nude into the snowdrift outside his cabin in the winter. On one occasion his companion, who had become somewhat annoyed with these outdoor activities, locked the door behind Pete as he leaped into the snow. In the very short time it took him to run barefooted around the house to the back entrance he developed frostbite on both his legs.

The human body itself can do very little to offset the cold. During prolonged exposure it endeavors to counteract the heat loss primarily by constricting the blood vessels, which decreases the heat conducted by the peripheral tissues until the skin has reached a certain temperature. Then shivering sets in, which may temporarily double the heat output. The core temperature of the body remains unchanged for a considerable time in spite of the cooling of the peripheral temperature, but eventually, if the heat debt continues, lowered body temperature (hypothermia) results, and—if untreated—will lead to death from exposure. The process of cooling is greatly accelerated when the cold is accompanied by wind.

With increasing cold, heat loss can be prevented by additional clothing up to a certain point. Beyond that point conventional arctic clothing becomes so bulky and clumsy that it is no longer practical. So far nothing we have devised has been able to equal the fur garments of the Eskimo, who can obtain greater insulation value with fewer layers of clothing. This is quite important, for in a critical situation the Eskimo can be fully dressed in a matter of seconds, while the white man will take several minutes to put on the many layers of his complicated apparel. Similarly, when moving into a warm shelter, the Eskimo removes his parka, and is comfortable, while the white man, in order to avoid perspiration, may have to discard layer after layer until there is a whole heap of clothes on the floor.

It is also a characteristic feature of Eskimo clothing that the air is allowed to circulate quite freely between the different layers, which facilitates the evaporation of moisture. Furthermore, the Eskimo parka is very loosely fitted, and the armholes are so large that the Eskimo may easily pull his arms out of the sleeves to warm his hands.

In the arctic, bedding is always carried on a journey, whether on land or on the sea ice, and a good sleeping bag is priceless. The usual type of "arctic" sleeping bag generally enables a man to sleep comfortably in temperatures down to −30° F. When it is colder than this, reindeer fur sleeping bags or bags of similar insulating value are highly desirable. On some of the most famous arctic journeys double two-man sleepings bags have been used to save weight and to conserve heat.

To produce adequate shelter under extreme arctic conditions is an art which requires considerable experience. In the olden days it was standard practice to build snow shelters of the well-known igloo type, particularly if one was traveling, for as the Eskimo had discovered without any knowledge of physics, snow is an excellent insulating material, i.e., a poor conductor of heat. The snow igloo is now very nearly a thing of the past. I have only once seen a group of Eskimo children practicing the art of building a snow house. Using the old-fashioned snow knife, they were working under the guidance of the old Eskimo Chief Akiviak, who in his earlier life had built igloos as a matter of course when traveling with his family. On the other hand, I have frequently seen an Eskimo hunter construct a simplified snow shelter when he was caught out by bad weather. Usually he scoops out a hollow in the snow, large enough to contain his sleeping bag, and erects over it a roof made from a few blocks of hard-packed snow. He lights his lamp, burning blubber with a wick of moss or other suitable material, to brew his tea and boil his meat. When he has finished cooking he reduces the heat of the lamp by removing part of the wick to make it narrower in order to conserve his fuel. This lamp is sufficient to keep his shelter snug and cozy.

Regardless of acclimatization, the success of arctic living and survival in the cold depends primarily on three factors: know-how, environmental protection and proper diet. These factors are of equal importance, for without knowledge and practical experience even the best equipment may be useless.

Know-how and practical experience are involved in every phase of arctic living, and are more often than not the factors which mean life or death. The experienced person keeps active in order to produce more body heat through muscular activity, while the inexperienced person stands still until his entire body is thoroughly chilled. In this condition he seeks refuge in his icy sleeping bag, and spends a miserable sleepless night. Or he may spend unreasonable amounts of energy—four hundred calories an hour—securing wood for a blazing fire, in front of which he will remain standing for hours, his front roasting, but his back, previously moist from sweat, icy cold. He fails to watch his face and hands, and without warning his nose turns white and is frost-bitten. I have seen this happen more than a dozen times. When removing his boots he may discover that his toes are hard as a board, for in many of the cases I have seen the patients state that the frostbite occurred without warning pains. Thus, before he knows it he is helpless and becomes a burden to the rest of the group.

Sweating may be exceedingly harmful when one is exposed to the cold. Once in Greenland I let myself break into a profuse sweat while dressed in a fur parka. I was chasing my dog team which had run off in pursuit of a bear. My shirt, which was soaked in sweat, froze into a coat of ice when I again was sitting on the sledge.

It is therefore important to learn how to prevent sweating by adjusting the amount of clothing to the degree of muscular work. The experienced traveler starts on the trail comparatively lightly dressed and sets a pace that is sufficient to keep him warm without perspiring. When making a halt, he buttons up his garments and adds additional clothing, including windbreakers if necessary, to keep from getting chilled by the wind.

Failure to realize one's own limitations may be fatal, and many an arctic traveler has fallen in his tracks by persisting in the face of blizzard and cold when even the dogs refused to go on, when their eyes were closed by the ice in their hairs, and their bellies gangrenous from frostbite. Under such conditions the natives of the North—the Eskimos—know it is futile to try, and wait patiently in their shelters until the weather has improved.

The history of arctic aviation is full of fatal accidents from which lessons may be drawn. For, unfortunately, many of these tragedies are caused by lack of experience and knowledge of arctic survival. A recent accident which happened to men I knew may prove the point: A crew of five took off in a twin-engined aircraft on a routine flight in Alaska in the month of February. The weather was very bad and they were flying on instruments when a strong wind took them off course, and they were lost in the middle of the night. For three hours they remained flying until lack of fuel forced them to bail out. Four men leaped into the unknown while the pilot remained at the controls, and then he too parachuted to the ground. That night the temperature dropped to —60° F. Weeks of search failed to find any trace of the missing airmen. They were found in the summer in the wild forests south of the Yukon. The pilot was a mile or so away from the aircraft, which was almost intact. His records indicated that he had lived with frostbitten hands and feet for about a week before he died. Three of the crew were found only a short distance away; their frozen bodies were lying in a heap, as if they had huddled together under a parachute, where they died with their shoes off. Most of them were inadequately dressed, but three distress fires had burned deep into the frozen tundra, and only a short distance away there was a log cabin which might have saved them all. The fifth member was never found. One may conclude that they had failed to use the first few moments after the safe landing to provide an effective protection against the cold. When their hands and feet became frostbitten it was too late and they lay down in the snow in front of the blazing fire, and froze to death.

In contrast to this, I remember the case of a pilot who was stranded somewhere along the upper Yukon under similar conditions, and survived. For many weeks he lived in this wild territory, walking downstream on the frozen river from one trapper's dugout to another, resting and feeding up on whatever edible products he came across on his way, until he eventually reached a small settlement from where he was returned to civilization.

The extreme heat loss that is possible in the arctic environment makes the question of heat production of particular importance, since, as I have previously explained, a negative heat balance over a prolonged period will result eventually in death.

It is well known that under usual conditions heat production in the Eskimo is significantly higher than in whites. The question arises whether this is due to a racial factor, or to factors peculiar to the Eskimo's way of living. In the latter case, there should be no reason why the white man could not produce the same amount of body heat, provided he adopts the Eskimo way of living.

In order to solve this question I was given the opportunity to carry out a series of metabolism studies under carefully controlled conditions at the Arctic Aeromedical Laboratory over a period of two years, from 1950 to 1952. For my tests I used a large number of Eskimos from four different settlements in Alaska, representing different climatic conditions, living habits and diets. Thus we were able to study the influence of race, diet and living habits on metabolism.

The first group at Barter Island, on the north coast of Alaska, lived on a diet consisting of approximately 50 per cent sea mammals and fish, and 50 per cent land mammals. The second group at Anaktuvuk Pass, located in the middle of the Brooks Range three thousand feet above sea level, lived almost exclusively on land mammals, especially caribou meat. The third group at Kotzebue, on the west coast of Alaska, lived to a considerable extent on white man's food, and their living habits were more affected by civilization than any of the other groups. The fourth group at Gambell, St. Lawrence Island in the Bering Strait, lived almost exclusively on sea mammals, and especially walrus meat.

These four groups were examined both in the winter and in the summer in well-equipped field laboratories which we established at the various Eskimo settlements. At Anaktuvuk Pass, a remote and inaccessible settlement, a great proportion of our equipment and supplies had to be para-dropped from the air. The rest of the equipment, including laboratory instruments which could not be dropped, was landed together with the personnel on a small lake by single-engine aircraft equipped with skis in the winter and pontoons in the summer.

As the result of these studies, we found, in agreement with previous workers, that by the first test the metabolism of the Eskimos living on their native diet is significantly higher than that of whites. The highest figures were observed among the most primitive Eskimos at Anaktuvuk Pass and Gambell, and the lowest figures obtained among the more civilized Eskimos at Kotzebue.

After having verified the results of previous investigators, the next problem was to explain the reason for the higher heat production in the Eskimo.

During our initial experiments we observed in several cases a reduction of over 20 per cent in heat production when the same subject was tested repeatedly on successive days, though living on the same diet. (The lowest metabolic rate was still higher than in the white controls.) We therefore interpreted the original high level as evidence of apprehension. In further studies we found that apprehension accounted for approximately 10 per cent of the high Eskimo metabolism.

We also observed that the Eskimo groups that had the highest metabolic rates also had the highest protein intake. The highest metabolic rates were observed at Anaktuvuk Pass among the caribou meat eaters where the protein metabolism was up to six times higher than that of normal whites. We also observed that the metabolism was higher in the winter, when the protein intake was increased, than in the summer.

The relation between the high-protein Eskimo diet and the high metabolic rate was, therefore, quite obvious. In order to discover exactly what that relation was, a special series of studies was carried out on representative Eskimo subjects from each of the four groups. These Eskimos were first studied in the field on their normal native diet, and then brought to our laboratory at Fairbanks, where the metabolism was again tested under carefully controlled conditions on several successive days while the subjects were eating the normal white man's diet. We found that in all cases the metabolic rates in the course of two to three days were reduced to the range of the normal white controls eating the same diet and examined under similar conditions. When the Eskimos were again given their high meat diet their metabolism increased to the initial values. In these experiments we were able to show that the specific dynamic action of the high-protein Eskimo diet accounts for approximately 15 per cent of the higher heat production in the Eskimo. In the case of the ordinary white man's diet, which is much lower in protein, the stimulating effect on metabolism of the evening dinner has disappeared after twelve to fourteen hours, while in the case of the Eskimo meat diet, enormously rich in protein, the effect lasts two to three days.

On the basis of these studies we concluded that there are no racial differences between the Eskimo and the whites in heat production. In this respect at least there is no reason why the Eskimo should get on any better than the white man in the arctic environment. Through generations the Eskimo has developed a liking for the high meat diet, which is the only possible diet in his situation, since meat is the main food product of the Arctic. In addition it has the advantage of its specific dynamic action, i.e., its greater ability to stimulate metabolism.

It has repeatedly been demonstrated that the white man, in his struggle to get along better in the hostile Arctic, may learn much from watching the Eskimo's way of living. It would seem natural to benefit from his nutritional experience as well.

Fortunately man possesses great nutritional adaptability, and the wide extremes in diet that are compatible with health are surprising. Thus, man can live comfortably on a meat diet, a vegetable diet or a combination of both. It has frequently been shown that arctic travelers normally accustomed to varied food may develop a liking for a meat diet (a mixture of protein and fat) when forced to live off the land, and can survive and maintain full working capacity on this food alone. On the basis of the generally accepted nutritional requirements in civilized conditions, this diet may appear highly inadequate, however.

The fact remains, nevertheless, that Nansen and Johansen maintained health and fitness on nothing but meat and blubber during their nine months in a stone hut in Franz Josef Land. They ate boiled bear flesh and soup in the morning, and fried steak in the evening. Sometimes they ate blubber with the meat, or dipped the pieces of meat in a little oil. At other times they ate burned blubber which they picked from the lamp. On this regime they not only remained perfectly healthy throughout the arctic winter, but they both gained considerable weight—Nansen twenty-two pounds, and Johansen thirteen pounds. Nansen writes with regard to their appetites: "We consumed large quantities at every meal, and, strange to say, we never grew tired of this food but always ate it with a ravenous appetite."

The fact that man can remain in good health on a diet of meat alone has further been convincingly proved by the eminent arctic explorer Stefansson. The evidence on which he clearly states this fact is ample and incontrovertible, and is drawn both from his extensive field study and from carefully controlled laboratory investigations, directed by Dr. E. F. Du-Bois at the Russell Sage Institute of Pathology in New York, when Stefansson and Karsten Andersen lived on nothing but meat for a whole year.

On the basis of the generally accepted views regarding the amount of Vitamin C needed by man, both Nansen and Johansen, as well as Stefansson and his companion, should have developed scurvy, since meat alone could not give them the quantities of Vitamin C usually recommended as the daily requirement. Although there may be a number of explanations for this phenomenon, the facts are still lacking.

While deficiency diseases have been common among white trappers in the Arctic who subsist mainly on imported foodstuffs, they appear to be practically unknown among primitive native Eskimos, who live entirely upon arctic animal organs and plants. It is therefore of interest to compare the Eskimo diet and its vitamin content with that of the arctic trappers.

We know that the Eskimo eats practically all the soft parts of animals such as seal, walrus, caribou, etc., with the exception of the gall bladder, urinary bladder, rectum and certain parts which are considered poisonous. The white trapper seldom eats any of the internal organs except the liver, and often even this is discarded. We also know that the Eskimo eats considerable quantities of both sea and land plants, such as seaweed, crowberries, roseroot, willow, mountain sorrel, thyme, saxifrage, harebell, dandelion, scurvy grass and angelica, while the trapper rarely eats any of them.

During the fifteen years I have studied arctic vitamin problems I have often been amazed to discover that all the internal organs and plants which have the highest vitamin content, especially Vitamin C, are considered particular delicacies by the Eskimo, and that though he knows nothing about vitamins some of his methods of preparing stored foods offer the best possible preservation of the vitamins. Thus, plants stored in blubber bags made of sealskins ("imigarmit") or stomachs, together with dried meat, boiled seal flippers, boiled narwhale skin, blubber or fat, and dried marine algae, have been found to contain most of their Vitamin C even after they have been kept in this way for months.

What people actually need in the way of food to keep healthy in the Arctic has by no means been firmly established. Several authors have suggested that individual caloric requirements would be about six thousand calories a day. A dietary survey which I conducted among European trappers in Greenland during the four seasons of the year, however, showed that the average person consumed only about three thousand calories a day, and I have recently obtained similar figures for whites and Eskimos in Alaska. These findings are of considerable practical consequence, for rations constitute a significant proportion of the load and on arctic journeys every pound of weight is important.

The fact that the trappers apparently require only half as many calories as experts have assumed would be needed under arctic conditions is probably because really hard physical work is only occasionally necessary—for instance when they are traveling on foot under difficult conditions. During the dark period of the year, when the food intake and calory consumption are at a very low level, the weather usually makes any exercise impossible. At times, the trappers are confined indoors for several weeks, and spend the greater part of the day resting in their sleeping bags in well-heated cabins. In the fall and early spring they travel by dog sledge along the fjord ice, and as the going is generally good, they are able to ride on the sledge during the journey, well protected by warm fur clothing. During the late spring when the fjord ice is breaking up and the snow is melting on the land, the trappers are again confined to the cabin. In the summer, they usually travel by motor boat, which does not entail hard work.

The total average energy expenditure of an adult Greenland Eskimo is estimated to be slightly less than three thousand calories daily, and similar figures were obtained for our Eskimos in Alaska. At the same time we determined that their average caloric intake was about three thousand calories a day. Again, this may be explained by the fact that the Eskimo does not normally go out in his kajak when the weather is bad, and he avoids traveling when the snow conditions are such that he must walk instead of ride comfortably on his sledge. Although he may occasionally do an enormous amount of work when the hunting is exceptionally good, most of the time he spends waiting for the game to appear or for the fish to bite. Furthermore, the Eskimo's clothing offers excellent protection against loss of heat.

It is a common misconception that Eskimo women and children lead a life full of strain and exposure to cold. Usually the Eskimo woman's work consists of sewing, preparing hides, dressing animals, storing food and so on, while the girls from the age of fourteen on help the women look after the children and pass the time with such activities as picking seaweed and sea mussels. The boys catch fish on the beach, practice paddling kajaks and throwing harpoons, or carry water. These tasks require only small amounts of energy. Under normal conditions the Eskimos spend the major part of the day lying or sitting about in their tents or in their houses where the temperature as a rule is higher than that found in the white man's houses.

It is interesting to note that the Eskimo's consumption of Vitamin A is almost ten times higher than that of the white trapper in Greenland. Since lack of Vitamin A reduces the power of night vision, upon which the arctic hunter must depend during the dark period of the year, the importance of a sufficient supply of this vitamin is evident. While I have never observed disturbances of night vision in Eskimos, several cases of reduced night vision associated with a very low Vitamin A intake have been reported among white trappers in the Arctic.

The main sources of Vitamin A in the arctic regions are the livers of sea and land mammals and fish. Of these we have found the liver of the polar bear to be the richest source of this vitamin, two ounces containing sufficient Vitamin A to supply the normal requirements of a man for a whole year.

Eskimos and arctic travelers have known for centuries that the polar bear liver is poisonous. This information was probably picked up by the early explorers and whalers from the Eskimos to whom it is traditionally taboo. I have noticed that when the Eskimos kill a bear they always carefully dispose of the liver to prevent their dogs from getting hold of it, either throwing it into the sea, burying it in the ground or putting it on the roof well out of reach.

The first report of poisonous effects of polar bear liver on whites dates back to the sixteenth century. Since that time numerous cases have been described among American, British, Danish and Norwegian explorers. The symptoms of the toxic effect are: violent headache, nausea, vomiting, reduced appetite, visual disturbances and peeling of the skin.

I began to study this particular problem in 1939, during a scientific expedition to Northeast Greenland, and collected samples of polar bear livers for the purpose of identifying the toxic substance. Preliminary examinations carried out at the Dunn

Nutritional Laboratories, Cambridge, in collaboration with Dr. T. Moore, disclosed the fact that these specimens were exceedingly rich in Vitamin A, and biological experiment led us to conclude that Vitamin A might be the cause of toxicity, giving rise to a condition called hypervitaminosis A.

During the summer of 1947 in Greenland I collected additional specimens of polar bear liver for examination at the Institute of Physiology, Oslo University. These livers showed the same huge concentrations of Vitamin A as the previous livers. Experimenting on rats, I was able to prove definitely that the toxic substance in the bear liver is identical with Vitamin A; for bear liver containing all its Vitamin A had the same effect as pure synthetic Vitamin A, when given in corresponding doses. Bear liver freed of its Vitamin A was harmless. Finally, the liver of a dog given large doses of pure Vitamin A until it contained as much as the bear liver had the same effect on rats as bear liver when given in the same amounts.

Identification of the toxic substance with Vitamin A may explain why small amounts of bear liver may be nontoxic, for in order to obtain a toxic excess of Vitamin A in man more than half a pound of bear liver has to be consumed. It also explains why bear liver appears to be less toxic when well cooked or fried, since in the process some of the Vitamin A is destroyed.

The practical conclusion to be drawn from this experiment is that while large doses of bear liver are harmful, it is an excellent source of Vitamin A when taken in small amounts.

The toxic effect on man of large doses of Vitamin A had never been observed before, and the early explorers and arctic travelers who suffered from the toxicity of polar bear liver were therefore the first provable cases of hypervitaminosis A in man. In 1943 Dr. Moore and I described a case of hypervitaminosis A in a man who had consumed large quantities of halibut liver oil. Since that time many cases have been described by other observers elsewhere. Most of them have occurred in America as the result of the eagerness of vitamin-conscious mothers to provide ample quantities of vitamins for their children. Under the motto "the more, the better," they have given them toxic doses of the very potent Vitamin A concentrates available on the market. In one hospital in New York in 1949 I saw eight cases of hypervitaminosis A in children.

The biological basis for "living off the land" in the Polar Basin has been reviewed in an earlier chapter. It might be justified, however, to add at this point that the recent discovery of the very high frequency of trichinosis in some of the arctic mammals has placed the problem in a different light. The microscopic roundworm, *Trichinella spiralis*, which is the parasite causing the condition, has been found to have a circumpolar distribution in man and animals, creating a major public health problem for which there appears to be no immediate practical solution. The infection of arctic sea mammals is sporadic but among land mammals, the polar bear and arctic huskies show an alarmingly high and dangerous incidence of trichinosis. Thus over 50 per cent of all polar bears examined showed trichinella infection. The reason for this high incidence has not as yet been definitely established. Nor is it known how long this situation has prevailed. If it had existed from the earlier times, it would be safe to assume that men like Nansen and Johansen, who lived almost exclusively on bear meat, would have suffered from trichinosis.

However, it should be borne in mind that although trichinosis can be a serious and even fatal disease, it can also be so mild as to escape diagnosis. Pathologists at the beginning of this century found evidence of previous trichinosis in a high percentage of all autopsies, often without the patient's history showing evidence of this disease.

An epidemic of trichinosis broke out among the personnel of a secret German weather station on Franz Josef Land during the last war. The fifteen men who acquired the infection from polar bear meat in the spring of 1944 became seriously ill and had to be evacuated by air for hospitalization. During the extensive trichinosis epidemic in West Greenland during the spring of 1947 approximately three hundred Greenland Eskimos were attacked and thirty-three died.

Comprehensive surveys have revealed a number of cases around the North Polar Basin, most of them traceable to polar bear meat, and it is interesting to note that even polar bears in captivity in zoological gardens have caused epidemics of trichinosis.

The significance of the problem is best illustrated by the ill-fated Andrée expedition in 1897 when trichinosis probably killed or contributed to the death of all three members of the expedition. From Andrée's diaries it is known that they killed and consumed a total of thirteen polar bears during their march across the drift ice from their abandoned balloon to White Island in the Spitsbergen Archipelago. A Danish physician, Ernst A. Tryde, has discovered evidence of *Trichinella spiralis* in the remaining muscle tissue of one of the bears found in their camp on White Island and has thus thrown new light on the mystery of the Andrée expedition fifty-five years after the death of its members.

It should be pointed out, however, that if the meat is thoroughly cooked or kept frozen for a sufficient period of time—thirty-six hours at −17° F. will suffice—the trichinella larvae are killed or made harmless.

Infectious diseases are rare among men isolated in the arctic environment. Under virgin arctic conditions there are few germs capable of producing disease unless they are brought in from the temperate zones. Once introduced into the isolated arctic communities, perhaps in garments or blankets, germs and certain viruses may survive the cold and cause the outbreak of epidemics of a serious nature when conditions become favorable. Isolated winter parties, for instance, seldom suffer from colds or influenza, but severe cases invariably occur following the arrival of the first ship from civilization in the summer.

Not even the Eskimos escape these epidemics. Most cases of infectious diseases among the Greenland Eskimos occur in the late summer and fall, the time of their principal communication with the outside world. In most cases the contagion is introduced by newcomers as a masked disease or through healthy carriers. A number of diseases such as influenza, whooping cough, scarlet fever, rheumatism, German measles, mumps, infantile paralysis and smallpox appear to develop in epidemics following contagion introduced from the outside world, while the occurrence of others, such as diphtheria, impetigo, typhoid fever, dysentery, various acute infectious gastroenteritis and infectious jaundice is sporadic, their contagion appearing constantly to be present.

Once the infection is introduced into the crowded Eskimo community it spreads rapidly, like an explosion, owing to the intimate intercourse between the people, the lack of cleanliness and hygiene. Smallpox has been known to exterminate very nearly the whole population of the districts attacked. Apart from the fatalities, an epidemic may be catastrophic if its onset coincides with one of the main hunting seasons, for it may prevent the hunters from securing the precious food. The result then is starvation and famine.

In his susceptibility to these diseases and in his clinical symptoms, the Eskimo is generally similar to the white man in a civilized community. However, the virulence of the germs that are introduced into the Eskimo settlements from outside may be greater than that of the germs constantly present in the community, to which the Eskimos have probably developed greater immunity.

Tuberculosis represents by far the most serious medical and public health problem among the circumpolar Eskimo population. There has been a tendency to blame the white race for the introduction of this malignant disease and it is a common belief among Eskimos that it never existed among the natives of the North prior to contact with the white man. According to the eminent Danish authority Dr. Bertelsen, however, the occurrence of tuberculosis among the native Greenland population was mentioned only a few years after the European colonization of the island in 1721, and the course of the disease then shows that it must already have been present for a long time.

Among the pathological conditions peculiar to the arctic environment, frostbite, snow blindness and the malignant cellulitis called spekk-finger (or sealer's finger or blubber finger) are of the greatest practical importance.

Frostbite is the result of actual freezing of the tissues, preceded by changes in the blood vessels caused by the cold. The freezing point of skin is in the neighborhood of −26° or −30° F. Frostbite will vary in severity depending on the degree of cold, the wind velocity, which is also an important factor, and the duration of exposure. Like burns, frostbite is clinically divided into three categories. It is called first-degree frostbite when only a localized superficial area is involved. In second-degree frostbite the damage is more extensive, with blister formation, and in third degree there is gangrene of the tissue with irreparable damage.

The pathology of severe frostbite is characterized by the death of the tissues. This is apparently due not only to direct tissue injury caused by the cold, but also to lack of circulation caused primarily by the contraction of the blood vessels.

In the case of frostbite, prevention is the essential part of the treatment. This is clearly recognized by experienced arctic travelers, who are extremely alert to frostbite, watching each other's faces for early signs of freezing: cessation of circulation as evidenced by a white patch of skin. When traveling alone one develops a habit of clutching the exposed part of the face with one's hands or of rubbing it with the back of the mitten, and of moving the hands and feet vigorously about at intervals. In Greenland I found it practical to use chewing gum when riding on the sledge. In this way I kept my face muscles in movement, and thus I was able to detect any early signs of numbness, evidence of the beginning of frostbite.

I have often heard people say that application of grease to the skin prevents frostbite, and that this is the reason why the Eskimos do not get frostbitten. The fact is, however, that grease rather increases the likelihood of frostbite, and when it gets on one's clothes it is likely to reduce their insulating value. Also, the Eskimos do get frostbite. It is true that they do not develop frostbite so quickly as most whites, but this is due to a number of factors, of which the Eskimo's extreme care in preventing it is of greatest importance.

I am convinced, however, that there is a difference between Eskimos and whites in their tolerance to cold. I have often walked side by side with Eskimos in the winter, facing a biting wind, but though we were dressed in similar clothes, the Eskimo would appear unaffected while I could barely stand the exposure. This, in my opinion, may be the result of a difference in the anatomical structure of the skin and in the blood circulation through the exposed parts.

On the other hand, I have seen several Eskimos with frostbite, developed when they were caught in severe weather while traveling, or when marooned on the drift ice. On one occasion I traveled by dog team with a party of Eskimos against a blinding blizzard in thirty below weather on St. Lawrence Island, and when we reached the village at the end of a twelve hours' fight against the weather, two of the Eskimos had frostbitten ears, nose and hands.

In the treatment of severe frostbite slow thawing as a rule is preferable; the older practice of rubbing the part with snow is to be condemned, for it only serves to increase the tissue damage. In the case of third-degree frostbite with gangrene, nature itself will eventually form a line of demarcation between live and dead tissue. I have seen cases of frostbite where the toes fell off and the lesion healed without the aid of a surgeon's knife.

Snow blindness may be a serious menace to the arctic traveler in the spring when crossing the wide expanses of white snow which reflect the burning rays of the intense sun. Under these conditions the use of sunglasses is a must, for this extremely painful complaint may develop quite suddenly, after a comparatively short exposure, even on slightly overcast days or in light fog. This happened to me once in Greenland during April, when traveling by dog sledge on the ice along the coast. I lost the only pair of sunglasses which I had brought on the trip when the sledge capsized among the hummocks in the pack ice in the morning. All day I traveled across the brilliant snow-covered ice, with my eyes unprotected.

In the afternoon I felt a stinging sensation in my eyelids, and by the time I made camp in the evening my eyes felt as if someone had thrown a handful of sand into them. A deep-seated pain developed in my eyes in the course of the night, and they had become so sensitive to light that I could hardly face the setting sun. I was forced to remain blindfolded in the tent until the symptoms improved sufficiently to enable me to go on. I improvised a pair of goggles in the Eskimo manner by carving two slits, large enough to admit a half-dollar coin edgewise, through a piece of wood, which I tied in front of my eyes with a cord. I was traveling down a valley with snow-covered slopes on both sides which reflected the sun in such a way that the rays hit me from all directions, but I endeavored to avoid the glare by looking as much as possible at dark objects such as the sled or the dogs. Since that time I have made it a rule always to carry an extra pair of sun goggles when traveling across the snow in the spring.

Spekk-finger (blubber finger) is the Scandinavian name for a severe type of finger infection, which is common among people engaged in arctic sealing. It has been known to Scandinavian sealers for generations. During one season, over 10 per cent of the crew of the Norwegian sealing fleet suffered from spekk-finger at the Spitsbergen sealing field.

The infection is of considerable practical and financial importance to the sealing industry, since the disease may incapacitate the patient for several weeks during the height of the sealing season. It is usually incurred during the skinning and the handling of the seal on the pack ice, or when the blubber is being removed from the skin on board the sealing vessels, but it may also occur among the men handling seal or unsalted sealskins at sealing stations ashore. I observed a typical case of this at the sealing station on Pribilof Island, Alaska. Severe hand infections resembling spekk-finger appear also to be frequent among some of the Eskimos.

When infected, the finger suddenly swells painfully. The skin becomes a reddish color, and has a somewhat taut and shiny appearance. The affected area is soft and swollen with a thick colorless fluid; but in most cases there is no pus. The patient complains of severe local pain and stiffness in the neighboring joints. I have seen cases where the pains were so severe that the patient himself had been forced to amputate his finger with a razor. Permanent damage to the finger bones from this condition has been demonstrated by X-ray.

The cause of the disease has not as yet been finally demonstrated, although several infectious agents have been isolated from cases of spekk-finger and from seals. I have been told by many sealing captains that it is particularly the older seals that are apt to cause the infection. In these animals infected wounds, scars and abscesses in the subcutaneous tissue are common.

Amputation of the infected finger was often necessary until recent investigation revealed that the condition could be successfully treated with modern antibiotics, especially aureomycin.

Next to the cold, the darkness of the arctic winter is perhaps man's greatest enemy in the rigid North. The psychological effect of the perpetual black or gray light when the stars, the moon and the aurora are the only guides in finding the trails across the colorless snow becomes of major importance, for a winter in the Arctic is more a psychological strain than a question of physical stamina.

Complete separation from the outer world, and the necessity of living wholly on the resources of one's small group, day after day, night after night, in all circumstances, through a seemingly endless darkness, make great demands on the nervous system. One's inner self is completely stripped and laid bare to the inescapable, sober truth. Self-centered man, stamped with life's fundamental principle, egoism, stands out, shorn of all civilization's trappings of polite phrases and assumed personality behind which lurks the instinct of self-preservation.

A man's reaction to this environment may be difficult to predict. For this reason it is hard to list the specific qualities, psychological or otherwise, that make a man best suited for arctic life. In general one may say that a balanced mind and a good physical condition are highly desirable.

Some men talk too much, others talk too little, and very many develop peculiar symptoms during the dark period of the year. Even one's best friends may turn out to be different in the gloomy atmosphere of a trapper's dugout, imprisoned by foul weather for days on end. I know two men who did not speak to each other for two weeks, although there was no one else to converse with. While one of them was preparing his meal, the other stayed in bed. When he had eaten, he threw the remaining food to the dogs, and went to bed so that his companion could get up and do the same.

Fridtjof Nansen for two hours spoke to the students of the University of St. Andrews in Scotland, many years ago, on the subject: "What We Dare Not Write in the Books." It was a dramatic lecture on the psychological effect of the arctic night. We can only imagine what it was like in the stone hut on Franz Josef Land where Nansen and Johansen spent nine months alone, their clothes and bodies smothered with dirty blubber and no soap to wash with so that their diaries became illegible from grease. The same thoughts came and went, with no more variety than their conversation, so they slept as long as possible to while the time away. The only variation in their routine was on Tuesdays, when they changed turns at being cook; the time was reckoned in cooking weeks until the spring. And yet, sharing all this agony, sharing even their one and only sleeping bag, they remained so formal throughout that they referred to each other by title.

Nansen and Johansen had these conditions forced upon them; it was a matter of bare survival. But the arctic trappers isolated in Greenland or on other remote arctic islands return to this sort of life year after year by choice of their own free will, and yet their winter nights must be almost as harsh on them psychologically as were Nansen's and his companion's.

In Greenland three of us were confined indoors for eleven days and nights; it was practically impossible to go outside the cabin door at any time. It was not so much the grim weather that upset us as the complete lack of privacy in the single tiny room where there was barely space enough to move about without bumping into one another.

At first it was pleasant not to have to go outside. There was much to be done in the way of reading and writing, mending and tidying up, and the time passed quickly. But after a while these tasks offered no occupation for one's restless mind. There was no difference between day and night. The tastiest food no longer attracted our usually greedy appetites. We started to play cards, but soon we had tried all the games we knew. Even the most interesting stories became dull, because they had been told too many times. We carefully avoided discussions because we all knew that they would lead to quarrels and catastrophe. Sleep became rare, and when we got up in the morning we no longer said, "Good morning," because this was obviously not the case. It was no longer necessary or even desirable to use words to express what we had to say; we could read it in each other's face, and so in the end we walked about in silence. And yet, through the fourteen months we lived together, never an unfriendly word was spoken.

In general it is preferable to live alone at such an arctic station, because then the daily routine jobs keep one constantly occupied; simply maintaining life requires all one's energy. In addition one may go to sleep when tired, eat when one is hungry, and work when it is convenient. After a while one thinks aloud and talks to oneself all the time. The advantage of this is that one always gets the right answers and is never contradicted!

I have often thought about the trappers, and wondered what makes them take up this extraordinary calling. No doubt for the majority it is a matter of necessity. The northern districts of Norway offer little natural wealth, and there are not many ways a man can earn his daily bread. From childhood these men have watched the sealing vessels leaving for the Polar Sea, and listened to the fascinating stories told by the trappers returning from Spitsbergen and other arctic islands with their catch. A great many of them like the free life which a trapping expedition offers. Some of them are escaping from an unhappy love affair, like those who in the old days joined the Foreign Legion. In many cases I feel sure that the desire for unusual adventures has been an important factor.

All the trappers I have met declare that they would never be content with the routine life at home and with regular working hours. During a long year of hard work they may have made a handsome sum of money. One trapper I met in Greenland was very proud of the fact that he had made a sum equivalent to the salary of the Prime Minister of Norway. They frequently spend it all within a fortnight after their return, and then start looking around for an opportunity to join another hunting expedition to the North.

Often I have heard them discuss their future plans, declaring that they would no longer spend their hard-earned money on wine, women and song. One was going to buy a small farm in the mountains, another was going to start a business and settle down; but as soon as they reached the home port and consumed the first case of whisky, their plans were "gone with the wind," and when the gay summer days came to an end, they found themselves once again in a humble trapper's cabin in the North.

One trapper I knew well spent $10,000 in three months. He hired a taxi as soon as he reached the port, and drove 250 miles to Oslo, where he met a famous actress, bought himself seven suits, seven greatcoats, a bowler hat and a walking stick with a silver handle. He lent money to all in need, and drank champagne from beer tumblers, in spite of the fact that in the Arctic he was a teetotaler. In three months he spent what he had made in seven years.

When my Greenland companion Rudi once returned from Spitsbergen with more than 130 bear skins, he hired a hotel and invited everybody who came by to come and stay as long as they liked. Fourteen days later the last skin was gone, and he was once again on his way to the North.

Probably some of the arctic trappers suffer from that introspective state of mind which feeds on its own imaginings and desires the least possible contact with others. It is possible that they also lack a social sense, and that they are running away from their fellow men. For men like these, in spite of the brutality of its climate, the Arctic may be called a protected environment. After all, a man's greatest enemy is his fellow man, whom he escapes by shutting himself into a cabin in the middle of the wilderness, where he may consider himself a person of great importance, able to mold his own destiny. Above all, such a person does not like to be commanded by anyone. He must do as he pleases. Some trappers even refuse to share their cabin with anyone else. They take risks and expose themselves to peril only when a man's life is at stake. But when someone is in danger—whether friend or foe—they do not hesitate to risk their own lives and safety in order to help.

Numbers do not seem to make much difference. Even in a larger group of men confined in a small mining camp or in an ice-bound ship, the psychological effect of the dark period of the arctic year is essentially the same. The arctic night has a tendency to bring out some of the less desirable elements in human behavior. Conceit, jealousy, suspicion, self-centeredness and egoism, excitability and an unbalanced disposition lead to scenes of violence and drama.

Once in Spitsbergen a man shot and killed his boss during a quarrel, merely because he was reprimanded. At a radio station in Greenland I saw the radio operator being chased by one of his companions with a knife, but he escaped by hiding under a table. The scene was caused by a dispute about a drink.

Nervous disorders and hysteria are not uncommon under these conditions, even among the natives of the arctic lands. Well known is the kajakphobia of the hunters who are suddenly struck by fear while out at sea in a kajak, and lose confidence in their ability to maneuver the tiny skin boat safely back to land. I have seen several hunters to whom this has happened who have refused ever again to venture out on the open sea in a kajak.

Various manifestations of the so-called "transitional madness" have been described by many arctic travelers. An Eskimo suddenly turns crazy and charges across the snow shouting and screaming, only to return after a while, perfectly calm and collected. Personally, I have never seen such a case, but I have known several Eskimos who had actually at one time or another suffered from this "transitional madness."

The Eskimo of today is mentally little different from the
white. In spite of his contented smile and appearance of happi-
ness, he shows in his village life the same evidences of pride,
jealousy and social intrigue that are common in any white society. They may take a slightly different form, but that is only
natural in light of his different standard of education and training. I once saw the entire native population of an Eskimo community, where life to the occasional visitor appeared perfectly
happy and harmonious, violently and actively involved in intrigue when an Eskimo widower competed with his own son-in-
law for the prettiest girl in the village.

The mental attitude of the men whose business it is to operate
aircraft through the leaden sky over the bleak wastes of arctic
snow and ice is subconsciously affected by their recognition of
the cold and darkness as factors influencing their chances for
survival in case of a crash or bail-out. This attitude is present
from the moment the mission is planned, it affects their preparations, it is reflected in the abundance of survival gear and
rations carried, and so determines the payload of the aircraft.

The study of the human factors in the arctic offers a new and
fascinating field of research of the greatest importance, for in
the northward expansion of the white race success rests with
man himself—and progress is limited to the abilities of man to
adjust himself to this new environment.

We know from experience that man can inhabit the arctic
world, for the Eskimo has successfully survived along the shores
of the Polar Basin for thousands of years with technical facilities
much inferior to those we possess today. It should be evident
from what has been brought out in this chapter that the reason
why the Eskimo gets along better than the white man in the
polar world is not essentially a matter of racial differences, or

real physiological acclimatization, but because he has adjusted or adapted himself in every respect to suit the environment. Since it is not likely that the arctic climate is going to change in the near future to suit human nature, we have no choice in our endeavor to exploit the arctic regions but to adjust the nature of modern man to the arctic climate. With the aid of our modern technical support this adjustment should be less difficult than it was to the Eskimo, who at one time had to get along with his stone knife and his flint.

From childhood the Eskimo is brought up to master the technique of arctic living. His mind is at ease, for he knows of no better life beyond the bulwarks of the frozen seas. By the time he is to face the elements alone, he is well versed in the art of arctic survival. Through generations he has developed a liking for his high meat diet which, as previously explained, stimulates his metabolism to produce a greater amount of body heat. His simple but practical garments of fur offer the best insulation, and his shelters are efficient in conserving the heat.

In our attempt to master the elements of the Arctic, we will do well to learn from the Eskimo's wisdom. But in light of the white man's ambitions in the Arctic—in peaceful world commerce, in the exploitation of hidden resources, in the struggle for strategic control and security—this alone will not suffice. We need to go further in our search for the scientific facts which affect human behavior in the Arctic.

We need to know what specific qualities, physiological and otherwise, are the most desirable in combating the arctic environment, and then we need to develop effective methods for selecting the most suitable personnel for arctic service. Further studies are required into the problem of acclimatization to cold, and its practical consequences. Details regarding nutritional requirements in the Arctic are still lacking, and the effect of the winter darkness on man warrants a closer study. Surveys of potential carriers of disease have to be made, and the problem of sanitation under various arctic conditions has to be solved. There is a serious need for better arctic clothing which can equal the Eskimo garments in practicability and insulating quality. We need to develop better shelters, and the capacity and efficiency of surface transportation need to be improved to meet the growing demands.

The classical era of polar exploration is over; the hope of discovering new lands and new trade routes no longer exists. The arctic explorer of today is concerned with the study of details which require the combination of field observations and highly technical laboratory research. In this respect the study of arctic problems offers the advantage of fascinating field experience combined with a search for new knowledge in a virgin field of science.

At the present rate of progress many of the practical problems confronting man in the Arctic may be solved within the next few decades. With the improvement of transportation and communication, life in the remote areas of the Arctic may in the future be little different from many of the communities in the temperate zones. Perhaps in years to come holiday resorts, rest homes, and sanatoria will be established in the Arctic, to which modern man may retreat from the hectic rush of city living. It is not without interest that among the natives of the North, the easygoing Eskimo people, high blood pressure, arteriosclerosis and peptic ulcers are extremely rare.

In order to establish the requirements for human survival in the North Polar Basin in the way of physical abilities, physiological and psychological factors, as well as food, clothing and shelter, much more detailed knowledge of the environment is essential. So far we know very little about conditions in the central Polar Basin, simply because it has, until recently, seemed impossible to penetrate into the heart of the Polar Sea to establish permanent bases for observations and scientific studies. The discovery of the ice islands offered the possibility of a new approach to this problem. As the ice island project materialized it was therefore only natural that students of the human factors joined with the other scientists and technicians in the new adventure.

CHAPTER EIGHT

Discovery of the Ice Islands

The existence of floating islands of ice in the North Polar Basin had been known to the United States Air Force for almost six years before we finally, in March, 1952, set out to establish a scientific base on T-3. It appears from old records that some of these tabular bergs were seen long ago by early explorers, who apparently thought they were ice-covered islands.

As we flew north on our way to T-3, I involuntarily searched the ice beneath us, for it was in this region that Peary saw his Crocker Land in the arctic mirage to the northwest of Ellesmere Island. In his records he describes the appearance of the faint outline of a distant land which he could barely discern through his glasses: "North stretched the well-known rugged surface of the polar pack, and northwest it was with a thrill that my glasses revealed the faint white summits of a distant land which my Eskimos claimed to have seen as we came along from the last camp."

It occurred to me that this fabulous Crocker Land must have been a floating island of ice, similar to that discovered by an air crew of the 46th Strategic Photo Reconnaissance Squadron in 1946. During a routine mission across the North Polar Basin from Ladd Field, Alaska, on August 14, an enormous heart-shaped object—some two hundred square miles in size—suddenly appeared on the radar scope at 76° 10′ N., 160° 10′ W., less than three hundred miles north of Point Barrow. A sensational message from the aircraft commander was flashed back to Washington in the night.

At the time, the existence of this huge object was classified secret, and caused considerable speculation about its nature, origin and probable future. It was designated by the name Target X, and later became known by the name Target 1 or T-1.

When it was first seen it was thought to be an island, for its radar scope return was similar to that of land. When on subsequent sightings its position had changed, it became obvious that the object was moving and could therefore not be an island. Visual observation on a clear day eventually revealed that Target X was a flat tabular iceberg floating free in the Arctic Ocean.

During the next three years Target X was followed by visual observations or by radar by aircraft of the 46th Strategic Photo Reconnaissance Squadron, and the 375th Weather Reconnaissance Squadron (now the 58th Strategic Weather Reconnaissance Squadron stationed in Alaska) flying their regular missions. By October, 1949, it had reached 85° 06′ N., 73° 00′ W., over fifteen hundred miles from its first reported position.

No one ever landed on Target X, so its characteristic features were known only superficially from high-altitude observations, and no other similar ice islands were discovered, although routine reconnaissance flights over the Polar Basin were in rapid progress during this period.

The potential scientific value of these ice islands was clearly realized, and in May, 1950, Lieutenant Colonel Joe Fletcher, commanding officer of the 58th Strategic Weather Reconnaissance Squadron, organized a concentrated search, with Major L. S. Koenig as project officer, for other ice islands in the regular track of the weather missions from Alaska to the North Pole, using radar as the primary tool for the search. In addition they kept continuous track of Target 1. Reports of objects claimed to be ice islands started to pour in, but careful examination revealed without exception that they were merely large ice floes.

Late in the night of July 21, 1950, Major Koenig returned from a mission with radar photographs of an object which he believed to be an ice island, at 86° 40′ N., 167° 00′ E. He called Colonel Fletcher in the middle of the night, and the two of them went down to the darkroom and developed the pictures. The excellent photographs left no room for doubt: they had discovered another ice island, about three hundred square miles in area, which they named T-2. It was later revealed that another crew of the squadron had observed T-2 two days earlier, but failed to realize that it was an ice island they had seen.

The search for ice islands continued, and finally, on the last day of July, 1950, Major Koenig came rushing to the hospital where Colonel Fletcher was having his appendix removed, with the radar photographs of T-3, discovered at 75° 24′ N., 173° 00′ W. This ice island was seen visually on August 24, 1950. During that mission the weather observer managed to take a photograph of a corner of T-3 in the clear weather, as they passed it at eighteen thousand feet, and for a long time this was the only source of detailed information of the surface characteristics of the ice island. During the subsequent missions cloud cover and darkness made visual search impossible until the following spring.

From the air the ice islands are readily distinguishable from the surrounding pack ice from great distances by their smoother surface and homogeneous appearance, and the ridged surface pattern with regular ridges and troughs running roughly parallel from one end of the island to the other. During the melting season several drainage systems with small streams cut across the troughs. In striking contrast to the surrounding pack ice, the ice islands remain of the same shape and size over a period of years, indicating the great thickness and firmness of the ice. The ice floes, on the other hand, are frequently broken up, and usually show evidence of pressure ridges and frozen leads.

T-1 has been described as shaped like a blunted arrowhead, fifteen by eighteen nautical miles. The photographs show very distinctly the fairly regular corrugations and the old drainage system. T-2 is squarer in shape, seventeen by eighteen miles in size, exclusive of the fringe ice, i.e., a thinner ice extremity protruding from one edge. It is clearly visible from the air seventy-five miles away. T-3 is shaped almost like a kidney, four and a half by nine miles in size. The corrugated appearance of the surface of T-3 is more marked, showing more relief, and it is much less regular. Low-level observations showed two dark spots on the surface, which to the observers in the aircraft looked like two piles of dirt from which dust had blown over the white snow.

The most characteristic features of these floating tabular icebergs are their massive proportions and great thickness—both T-1 and T-2 being larger than the island of Guam—the strikingly regular pattern of the surface relief resembling the corrugations of a tin roof, and their peculiar wedge shape, similar to the blade of an axe, one side being higher than the other, and the surface gently descending to the opposite edge.

It has been suggested that T-3 is the youngest of the three ice islands, and that T-2, which is smoothest, has floated in the Polar Basin longest. The conclusion is based on the assumption that during the summer the water produced by the melting on the ridges is collected in the troughs and depressions, where it refreezes so that the relief of the undulating surface is gradually reduced. This process may be repeated year after year with a progressive cycle of melting and freezing.

The surfaces of all three floating ice islands have been scanned by three different experienced aircraft commanders, who agree that a forced landing, wheels up, would be feasible on all three islands.

The discovery of the ice islands was first made public in a report presented by Colonel Fletcher at the First Alaskan Science Conference in November, 1950. At this time, the 58th Reconnaissance Squadron was granted authority to fly special missions in addition to the regular weather missions in order to track the known ice islands, and to search for new ones. On the basis of this authority, the squadron carried out an extensive reconnaissance program of the Arctic Ocean north of Alaska and the Canadian Archipelago between the 30° W. and 180° W. meridians.

The months of March and April were chosen for the flights, to take advantage of the favorable conditions usually encountered during that particular period of the year, with a combination of daylight and minimum cloudiness. In spite of this active search program with a series of long missions between March 14 and April 30, no new ice islands were discovered.

On August 1, 1951, the weather was at last ideal for a major flight to the area of T-1 and T-2, and the mission known as Ptarmigan special Roger was flown, with a weather reconnaissance B-29 aircraft. The weather remained perfect for visual observation throughout the flight which lasted about twenty hours.

During the approach to Ward Hunt Island north of Ellesmere Island, a large mass of ice was sighted about fifty miles north of the island. On closer examination this proved to be T-1, which at that time had been lost for twenty-two months. From an altitude of 18,000 feet they descended to 250 feet and made two low passes across the entire ice island. They found the surface surprisingly flat, with a gently rolling pattern. From the air there appeared to be running water in some of the drainage channels, but the water in the large parallel troughs appeared to be frozen solid.

A few hours later T-2 was sighted at 87° 07′ N., 25° 00′ W., and a low-level investigation was made. As the heavy aircraft roared across the floating island only one hundred feet above the ice, the crew members were amazed at the smoothness of the surface. The island, almost twenty miles long, appeared as flat as a table, and the clear blue ice was visible over large areas. The pilot, who was a very experienced flier, stated that he would have had no objection to land the B-29, wheels down, on the island provided he had fuel enough to get back home safely.

The observers estimated that the height of the island above the surrounding pack ice was in the vicinity of thirty feet. And some of them insist that they saw a seal jumping off the edge as they thundered over its head.

The extensive ice reconnaissance performed by the 58th Reconnaissance Squadron had indicated that ice islands in the sector between 30° W. and 180° W. and north to the Pole are not so frequent as one would be led to believe by the discovery of two such islands in the same area in the course of a single summer; for while covering about 400,000 square miles of the Polar Sea no new ones were found.

The movements of T-1 were followed fairly regularly from August, 1946, to October, 1949. During this period of thirty-eight months it covered a distance of 1,400 miles at an average

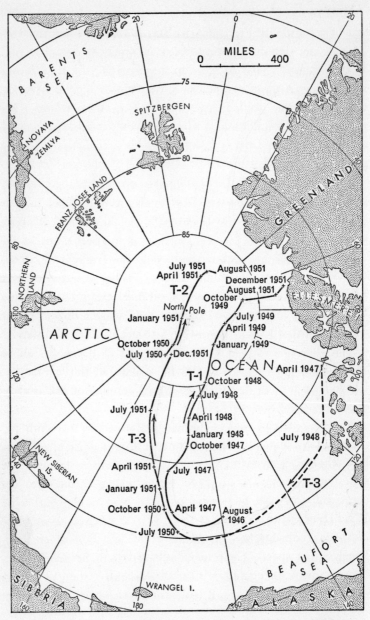

The Paths of the Ice Islands: T-1, T-2, T-3 (August '46 to December '51)

rate of approximately 1.2 miles per day. T-2 moved approximately 1.1 mile per day during the forty-seven weeks it was observed. It moved from a position close to the center of the Polar Basin straight across the geographical North Pole to a point between the Pole and the northern extremity of Greenland, where it remained more or less stationary for one year. It was last sighted on August 1, 1951. During a fifty-four-week period when T-3 was regularly observed it drifted at a rate of 1.3 mile per day.

From the scattered observations, we can piece together the general pattern of the movement of the ice islands, which in turn is an indication of the general trend of the currents in this part of the Polar Basin.

As far as can be judged on the basis of the available evidence, the ice islands drift about in the Polar Basin clockwise from Ellesmere Island, westward north of Alaska, turning north of Bering Strait, floating more or less across the Pole, turning south again toward Ellesmere Island or Greenland. They apparently escape the influence of the East Greenland Current, which would have carried them to certain destruction in the Atlantic. I have been told, however, that once during the last war a body of ice, supposed to have been an ice island, reached the waters south of Greenland, where it collided with numerous ships.

From the regions north of Ellesmere Island there appears to be a relatively slow drift westward carrying the ice islands to the area north of Alaska, although recent evidence indicates an occasional eastward movement close to land in the region of Ward Hunt Island. When they reach 175° W. there is a northerly movement carrying the ice islands across the Pole at comparatively great speed. Their movement seems to be retarded as they approach Greenland or Ellesmere Island.

When T-2 was last seen it had been at a standstill for a year.

Its future movement is difficult to predict, for apparently it is in an eddy between two currents—the East Greenland Current, and the presumed current that might bring it, like T-1, back toward Ellesmere Island. T-2, however, is much further out toward the East Greenland Current than T-1 has ever been, and it seems likely that its future course will be down the east coast of Greenland, in which case it should be watched for closely, as it would represent a danger to shipping in the North Atlantic.

It appears that there may be a difference between the movement of the ice island and that of the surrounding pack ice. This may not be surprising in view of the fact that the ice islands extend further below the surface than the surrounding pack ice, so that the deeper currents have a greater effect on them. On the other hand, the smaller floes in the pack ice would be more quickly affected by a change in the direction of the wind than the heavier ice islands. These circumstances and the fact that the islands can be so easily recognized among the pack ice make them very valuable in the study of Polar Sea currents and the relation between wind and current.

A year after T-3 was discovered in July, 1950, Colonel Fletcher came across a photograph of a piece of "land ice" near the Isachsen Peninsula, Ellef Ringnes Island, at 79° 50′ N., 104° 00′ W., taken during a joint USAF/RCAF flight by Squadron Leader Keith R. Greenaway in 1947. Colonel Fletcher was struck by the resemblance between this "land ice" and T-3, and by comparing the photographs he was able to determine that they were the same. During the period from April, 1947, to July, 1950, T-3 had moved a distance of approximately a thousand nautical miles, averaging almost one mile a day.

As a result of the interest created in the ice islands by the USAF activities in the Polar Basin, the Canadians re-examined their large number of photographs taken during joint

USAF/RCAF flights in the Canadian Arctic. The results have been published by Squadron Leader K. R. Greenaway in *Arctic*, July, 1952.

An ice island photographed on July 9, 1948, from a USAF aircraft engaged in survey photography near the west coast of Prince Patrick Island also turned out to be T-3. Furthermore, the USAF survey photographs revealed two other large tabular bergs in the Arctic Ocean, apparently different from any of the known ice islands. One was photographed on June 28, 1948, at 82° 45′ N., 104° 30′ W., northwest of Axel Heiberg Island, and was about seven or eight miles long and six or seven miles wide. It has never been observed since. The other ice island, which has also been lost since 1948, was first photographed in July, 1947, off Cape Columbia on the north coast of Ellesmere Island, and appears to have drifted eastward, close to the shore, for it was again photographed in May, 1948, twenty miles east of its previous position. This ice island is of special interest because the photographs apparently reveal the place from which it originated, the same series showing a gap in the shelf ice near Cape Nares where a large section of the shelf appears to have broken away. Two sides of the ice island could be fitted into this gap like a piece of a jigsaw puzzle.

In addition to these, according to Greenaway, twenty-eight ice islands varying in size from a quarter of a mile to seven or eight miles across have been found by the examination of the RCAF trimetrogon photographs.

In early arctic literature one finds many references to "ice islands." However, the meaning of the name is not always clear in the confusing terminology of some of the early arctic explorers. A bibliography of references to ice islands has already been published by Moira Dunbar in *Arctic*, July, 1952.

Parry in 1821 speaks of an immense floe in M'Clure Strait, estimated to be forty to fifty feet thick, with a surface resembling "hill and dale." A similar ice mass in the same area, off Cape Providence, was described by Robert S. Janes in 1910. Greely in 1883 observed floes fifteen miles long, with a surface resembling rolling country, near Cape Baird. Nansen describes a tabular ice floe which looked almost like an island covered with ice, north of Franz Josef Land. Otto Sverdrup has described ice formations of similar nature off the coast of Ellef Ringnes Island.

Of particular interest is Storkerson's drift on an unusual ice floe in the Beaufort Sea north of Alaska from April to October, 1918. Storkerson was in charge of a party of four members of Stefansson's Canadian Arctic Expedition. On March 15 they had set off with eight thousand pounds of provisions and equipment from Cross Island over the ice for the purpose of reaching 77°-78° N., from which point they would make a great circle course east toward Prince Patrick Island. On April 8 they were stopped by a large open lead at the edge of an unusually large floe. Here they changed their plans and settled to drift in the Polar Sea, on April 16.

For seven months they drifted about in the Beaufort Sea on this large island of ice, which was about seven miles wide and over fifteen miles long. Storkerson says that in relation to the smaller surrounding floes it acted exactly as land does. The smaller floes were more easily affected by a change in the direction of the wind, so that open water formed between the floe and the pack ice, in which they had an excellent opportunity for hunting seal.

Storkerson gives the following description of the ice floe: "From an elevation close by our camp the panorama presenting itself impressed me exactly as that of a certain kind of land. The color of course was the bluish white of ice, but the contours of the hills, the ridges and the levels in between and in which numerous lakes and ponds were visible was exactly like certain stretches of prairie I have seen in the Midwestern United States and Canada. This similarity of old ice to land is well known.

"The thickness of the ice at our camp, judging by the amount of it visible above the level of the sea, I should say would be about 50 or 60 feet. This extraordinary thickness was just local and the average of the whole floe would be much less, probably less than 20 feet."

From this description the striking resemblance between Storkerson's old ice floe and the ice islands is evident.

Cook has described an ice formation in the Arctic Ocean which might well have been an ice island. For two days they traveled over old ice without pressure ridges and hummocks. He states that it was impossible to determine whether they were on land or sea ice. The ice had "the hard, wavering surface of glacial ice, with only superficial crevasses."

In September, 1931, an Eskimo, Takpuk, landed on what he thought was an island—Takpuk Island—in the Beaufort Sea, about half a mile long, with a rolling surface where there were small ponds of fresh water. The highest point was about forty to fifty feet above sea level. Extensive flights over the assumed position of this island have failed to verify its existence, and it would not be surprising if what the Eskimo discovered was a floating island of ice, although he reported the presence of grass and mosses.

A tabular berg similar in appearance to the ice islands has been observed locked in Independence Fjord in Northeast Greenland, between the Margarethe and Princess Thyra Islands. It was photographed from the air in 1950 at an altitude of one thousand feet. According to Count Eigil Knuth, leader of the

Danish Pearyland Expedition 1947-1950, who visited the area in 1949 and again in 1952, it is so flat that it can hardly be seen from the fjord ice. It has been suggested that this berg is a relic of a small ice cap which once covered the islands and extended seaward.

Of considerable interest in this connection is the calving, observed in recent years, of the huge glacial shelf extending from the Braasvell Glacier several miles out to sea at the east coast of Spitsbergen. It looks as if the edge of this glacier tongue, rising up to perhaps fifty feet above sea level, is in part floating free on the ocean.

The origin of the ice islands has puzzled the glaciologists from the time they were first discovered, and a number of different theories were first advanced. Although the actual thickness of the ice remained unknown, since no one had ever landed on such an island, it appeared to be about several hundred feet. It is obvious that ice of such thickness could not have been formed as sea ice; nor, because of their tremendous dimensions, was it likely that they were regular icebergs formed by the calving of ordinary glaciers reaching the sea.

Colonel Fletcher, who was in charge of the ice island search as commanding officer of the 58th Reconnaissance Squadron, devoted most of his spare time during the winter 1950-1951 to searching arctic literature for a clue to their origin. The phenomenon of the "shelf ice" or the "glacial fringe of Grant Land," described by Peary, along the northern coast of Ellesmere Island was first brought to his attention by Y. Glenn Dyer of the U.S. Weather Bureau and Major Donald Shaw, USAF Arctic Desert Tropic Information Center at the Air University. This led to some interesting considerations, for as later studies have revealed, the shelf ice is almost the only possible origin of the ice islands.

After Peary had returned from his unsuccessful attempt to reach the North Pole in 1906, he traveled the whole length of the north coast of Ellesmere Island and describes the wavy ice west of Point Moss, extending for a distance of over two hundred miles and in places stretching as much as thirty miles from land. The junction between shelf ice and pack ice was indistinct so that often he was unable to make out where the shelf ice ended and the sea ice began. West of Point Moss, he encountered for the first time what later becomes a constant feature of the glacial fringe—"the long, prairie-like swells of its surface." "These swells," he continues, "are on a large scale, and reminded me very strongly of portions of the ice-cap of Greenland." Later on he writes: "The glacial fringe here has a distinct glacial characteristic in that its surface is undulating, and there is a gradual descent in going away from the land."

When describing his start from Ellesmere Island for the Pole in 1909 he writes: "For a few miles only after leaving the land we had level going, as for those few miles we were on the 'glacial fringe.' This fringe, which fills all the bays and extends across the whole width of North Grant Land, is really an exaggerated ice-foot; in some places it is miles in width. While the outer edge in places is afloat and rises and falls with the movement of the tides, it never moves as a body, except where great fields of ice break off from it and float away upon the waters of the Arctic Ocean." From his description it seems that Peary witnessed the breaking off of the floating islands of ice, and has given the answer to their origin and formation.

On the night of March 19, 1951, a B-29 flew a special mission to these regions, and discovered that the entire coastline of Ellesmere Island from Nansen Sound to the turning point near Ward

Hunt Island was largely covered with ice similar in nature to that on T-3, with the familiar corrugations.

The assumption is that the shelf ice is a relic from a period of extensive glaciation which apparently occurred after the last ice age. As time went on the shelf ice dwindled, became more fragile, partly isolated, and started to break off in the sections particularly exposed to the action of the tides, swell, and the pressure of the sea ice. I was told by the Eskimo chief at Barter Island, Andrew Akootchook, that once in the winter of 1933 a violent gale swept all the ice away from the coast, and swells rising to enormous heights rolled against the shore. Under circumstances such as these, large fragments of the floating outer edge of the shelf ice might well break off.

Since Peary's time this must have happened frequently, and the shelf must have dwindled with the general recession of the arctic glaciers, for as we flew over the northern shore of Ellesmere Island in the spring of 1952 the "glacial fringe" appeared to be far less extensive than in 1906, when it extended much further west.

From all available evidence, then, it seemed almost certain at the time we were planning the landing on the ice island T-3 that these tabular bergs were born of the shelf ice on the north coast of Ellesmere Island. Further evidence obtained during the expedition supported this theory.

CHAPTER NINE

Project Icicle

Since the ice islands rotate in a circular course through the least known part of the North Polar Basin, their value as steppingstones in the exploration of the Basin was obvious. Scientists stationed on one of these islands would be able to carry out continuous studies as it moved along its path, and cover large areas of the Polar Sea. In addition, the ice islands, unlike the regular pack ice, were apparently solid and persistent bodies which would afford a secure base not likely to be destroyed by pressure created by wind and weather.

This fact was recognized by the United States Air Force, and the Alaskan Air Command had considered plans for a landing on the ice islands every year since they were first discovered in 1946. The Air Force's interest may be easily understood by those who remember General Henry H. Arnold's famous address to the United States Military Academy at West Point in 1946, when he declared:

"The first line of the nation's defense lies now to the North, between America and that attack which will surely come from over the Pole.

"From that trans-polar air attack, no land army or naval force can defend the nation.

"To meet that attack, to throw it back, and to counterattack the enemy in his homeland military vitals, the American people must look to airpower—airpower over the North Pole, the strategic center of our world today."

The Alaskan Air Command, with its headquarters in Anchorage, is not only charged with responsibility for a vital part in the defense of the arctic approach to the American continent and the solution of strategic and tactical problems of arctic operations. It is also concerned with the collection of important weather data essential for long-range weather predictions, as well as search and rescue activities in its arctic field of operations. The mission of the Alaskan Air Command finally includes the initiation and support of research and development pertaining to the many technical and human problems connected with Air Force functions in the Arctic.

In order to accomplish this mission, the Alaskan Air Command had to extend its air operations into the heart of the North Polar Basin. It therefore became necessary to find out to what extent the polar ice could be used for the landing and take-off of heavy aircraft.

The first ice landings ever made with the twin-engined ski-equipped C-47's on the polar pack ice were carried out by the 10th Air Rescue Squadron on the initiative of Colonel Bernt Balchen, in the spring of 1950. These operations confirmed the Russian experiences from 1937 that landings on the floating drift ice were practicable.

Encouraged by these successful experiments, the 10th Air Rescue Squadron in February, 1951, went ahead to set up a permanent station on the regular pack ice about one hundred miles north of Alaska. This station, which was to be maintained on a year-round basis, was a link in an extensive plan for a series of similar stations on the pack ice for search and rescue and aerial support of advanced bases.

The party of eight men landed on a frozen lead three miles broad and nine miles long. They were under the direction of Captain Mike Brinegar, who later was one of the first three members of the T-3 expedition. They built their camp, consisting of four Jamesway huts, equipped for weather observations, with radar, navigational aids and other facilities, near the edge of a thick floe of old sea ice, and established radio communication with the mainland.

For twenty-two days the station was in full operation, and all went well. Then suddenly on the morning of the twenty-third day a strong gale developed; the floe broke and a two-hundred-foot-broad crack opened close to the camp. With a thundering roar the two pieces were set together, closing the lead under terrific pressure and grinding away the ice along the crack. The entire ice field trembled and shook.

The horrified crew radioed for help as they fled from the might of the ocean. From a distance they watched their camp being chewed apart bit by bit as the hours passed. Sky-reaching hummocks were turned on end and broke in over their huts, which were smashed to pieces and finally sank into the sea with the rest of the equipment through the cracks in the ice. The drama reached its climax when a fifty-foot lane formed right through the camp, splitting the ice floe in two and shattering the landing strip. The C-47 which came the same day to rescue the party had to make a hazardous landing on a smaller frozen lead three miles further north.

After this catastrophe plans for further operations were abandoned. Although the annihilated base had been set up on a regular ice floe in the drift ice, it was a common misconception, resulting from the inaccurate press publicity, that this particular floe had been an ice island. This was very unfortunate indeed, for the memory of this ill-fated project naturally served to dampen enthusiasm when plans for landing on the ice islands were later submitted.

In the spring of 1951, however, preparations were actually made by the 10th Air Rescue Squadron for a landing on the ice island T-3, which at that time, according to radar observations made by the 58th Weather Reconnaissance Squadron, was only some seven hundred miles north of Point Barrow. The operation was delayed by bad weather, and when a final reconnaissance mission failed to find T-3 at the reported position, the project was abandoned.

During the period from 1950 to 1951 my duties with the Arctic Aeromedical Laboratory at Ladd Air Force Base, Alaska, included various physiological studies involving fliers from the 58th Reconnaissance Squadron engaged in routine flights from Eielson Air Force Base, Alaska, to the North Pole. In the course of these studies it sometimes was necessary for me to go along on the flights, and I became well acquainted with Colonel Joe Fletcher, who at that time was commanding officer of the squadron. More often than not our conferences on physiological problems of polar flying ended with lengthy discussions of the nature of the ice islands and of how they could be utilized as bases for the exploration of the North Polar Basin.

One day in December, 1951, Joe Fletcher walked into my laboratory quite unexpectedly, as I was about to set out on a field study of arctic survival rations. He looked as if he had something unusual up his sleeve, for he grinned as he pulled a stack of photographs and maps out of his bag and put them in front of me on the table. Then he told me the news:

"Finally!" he said. "The Alaskan Air Command has decided to try to set up a base on one of the ice islands in the spring. I've been appointed project officer, and General Old is determined that this time it will be a success."

He paused, to give me a chance to recover from my surprise. Then he asked if he could count on me to take part in the project to help him with the planning and the preparations and to accompany him during the initial landing. It would be my job to take care of the rations, the medical problems and the equipment for the initial landing. I would also be concerned with the practical procedure of survival on the ice island during the initial phase.

I must admit that this was a chance I had long waited for, the kind one does not run across often in a lifetime. The very prospect of taking part in such a unique expedition would have been enough to fill me with excitement a few years earlier. When I was first picked to take part in an arctic expedition at the age of twenty I was prepared to give up anything for the arctic adventure. Now it was different. First of all the Arctic was no longer so new and unknown to me; and above all I had certain obligations at home, for my wife expected our first baby at the time the landing was scheduled to take place. I was therefore reluctant to leave.

It is customary among some of the fliers in Alaska to obtain what they call "kitchen clearance" from their wives when they are about to embark on an unusually hazardous operation. I found it natural to adopt this procedure in my case, and left the decision to my wife, who had been working as my laboratory assistant. She settled the problem, pointing out that when babies are being born men are not only superfluous but often even a nuisance!

Joe Fletcher was in the same predicament as I. He had, in fact, already sent his wife back to the States, as his first move in the ice island project.

We were now free to roll out the maps and to begin our preparations for the operation, which was given the name "Project Icicle." In the weeks and months that followed, our discussions continued night after night as the plans were made and altered in accordance with the ever-changing circumstances.

During the daytime we were usually busy trying to obtain the necessary equipment and supplies. Joe was constantly on the run from one office to another, briefing, arguing, persuading and obtaining support.

The decision to make the thirty-one-year-old Joe Fletcher project officer was indeed a fortunate one; for no one could have accomplished the difficult task of planning and organizing the complicated logistic support better than he. He possessed enthusiasm and a personal interest in the problems involved, developed in the course of his duties in Alaska. He had a scientific background from his training at the University of California, and his previous assignments at Air Force Research Centers including the Geophysical Laboratory at Cambridge, Massachusetts. In addition, he had experience and the ability to stimulate a heterogeneous group of people to work co-operatively and to their utmost. His leadership and unselfish devotion to the task were an example to the entire group.

In the evenings, at the end of a strenuous day, he would often turn up at my house to go through the program and to work out our list of supplies. Many a time our discussions went on until the early hours of the morning, as we tried to iron out the problems that continually cropped up.

The first question was which of the ice islands to select as our target. The selection had to be made in the light of what we knew about the ice islands at the time, and in each case the hazards and the obstacles had to be carefully weighed against the possible advantages. We had to make up our minds about the number of men who should take part in the initial and subsequent operations. We had to think of what to do in case of an emergency at any one of the many stages of the actual air operation—how to survive, what emergency gear to take along, what food to carry and what shelters to use. The problem of communication had to be solved, and finally we had to prepare the ground for the scientific studies which were to follow when the station had been established. We kept my wife busy searching arctic literature for specific items of information which we needed, such as the earlier records of temperature, wind, and snow cover, and the occurrence of animal life in the regions we would operate through.

The success of any arctic expedition depends first and foremost on the thoroughness of the preparations. And to prepare for an arctic expedition is often as interesting as the actual expedition itself, particularly when the regions to which one is bound are comparatively unknown.

At that time, T-1 and T-2 had last been seen in the fall of that year, and T-3 was slowly approaching the North Pole. It was anticipated that T-3, at the present rate of movement, would reach the Pole sometime in March or April, 1952.

From the standpoint of exploration and scientific studies, we realized that T-3 would be our most desirable target because of its location near the center of the North Polar Basin. But from what little we knew about its surface, and from the photographs we had to go by, it was undoubtedly the most difficult one to land on. In addition, its great distance from the nearest land base, Alert, Ellesmere Island, would create a difficult problem from the point of view of the air operations. T-2 was smoother and therefore better from an operational standpoint, but its position made it less useful for our project, for in all probability it would take a course to the east into the Atlantic with the East Greenland Current, and thus escape from the Polar Basin in a matter of months. In that case a station on T-2 would be of greater interest to shipping than to the scientists concerned with the comparatively unknown area of the North Polar Basin north of America. T-1, last seen in August, 1951, appeared to be stranded or at least fairly stationary off the north coast of Ellesmere Island, only some one hundred miles from the nearest weather station at Alert, so it too would be of less importance than T-3. In all probability a scientific party on T-3 would, in the course of the next few years, have an opportunity to study the greater part of the Polar Sea between North America and the Pole. Furthermore, T-3 was moving along very close to the regular "Ptarmigan" track flown by the 58th Weather Squadron from Alaska to the Pole, which would facilitate communications with the party and add to the factors of safety in case of an emergency. In addition, T-3 had been almost continuously followed for a considerable period of time.

Before any final decision could be made, it was necessary to locate T-1 and T-2. For this purpose, a special mission was flown with Joe as the aircraft commander, on the 21st of December, 1951. I went along as an observer.

I drove from Fairbanks to Eielson airfield in the middle of the cold dark midwinter night and arrived in the mess hall at 6:30 A.M. to share the preflight breakfast with the crew. They had already lined up in their electrically heated suits and heavy arctic flying clothing in front of the "chow line" for their cereal, fruit juice, coffee and hot cakes. Stragglers stamped the snow off their feet as they entered with a gust of the chilling ice fog which was rolling in through the rime-covered door. In the gleamy light we gathered around the table where Joe was sitting reading a book, and while we ate we talked about ice.

At 7:00 A.M. we gathered in the hangar where the co-pilot, Major James F. Soderburg, with whom I had flown to the North Pole before, and his crew of engineers were in the process of checking the superfortress. Not an inch of the huge giant, whose wings almost reached from one wall to another, appeared to escape their attention. The standard survival gear and rations were taken aboard. We put on our heavy flying clothes and parachutes and then the co-pilot inspected each member of the crew before we boarded the aircraft. First came, in order of importance to the mission, the pilots, followed by the engineer, the navigators, radar operators, and the weather observers, with me at the end. Of this entire crew Joe and I were the only ones who eventually took part in the actual T-3 expedition.

Then the doors were closed behind us, the brakes taken off, and the aircraft was slowly pulled out of the hangar. The engines were started, one by one, and roared through the still air. A few minutes later we taxied to the end of the runway, where the bright runway lights were sparkling in the gray twilight of the early winter morning. Again one by one the engines were run up, then came the signal for each man to take his appointed take-off position. We began to roll forward as the throttles were opened; Joe fought the controls as the plane roared down the snow-covered runway between the lights, pulled by the thundering engines. Almost unnoticeably we were lifted from the ground and began to fly, heading north toward the arctic coast of Alaska.

Black smoke poured from No. 3 engine as we were climbing, but as we leveled off and reduced power the smoke disappeared.

We were flying in the arctic twilight above the clouds where only the highest peaks of the mountains in the Brooks Range protruded through the mist. I was watching the snow-covered nunataks shining in the moonlight when the voice of the left scanner suddenly reported: "No. 2 engine is on fire." I looked out and saw flames licking the wing from the engine.

The monotonous routine was suddenly broken, and gave place to a few moments' hectic activity among the fliers, some of whom were brutally awakened. Orders flashed back and forth. The gas flow to No. 2 engine was cut, and the propeller feathered. The fire was extinguished when we turned about and made for home.

We buckled on our parachute harnesses just in case, for No. 4 engine was also running rough and had a leakage in the exhaust pipe. After two hours and twenty minutes' flight we landed.

Another attempt was made on Sunday, December 23, and this time we had more success. It was snowing as we took off with gas for twenty-three hours' flying. We encountered strong head winds and severe icing conditions and were forced to climb above the sky cover north of the mountains. From Alaska we flew eastward, heading for the northwest corner of Ellesmere Island, and then followed the Ellesmere coastline eastward, so that we had the contours of the coast on the radar screen all the time. In the distance to the south the huge snow- and ice-covered mountain range of Ellesmere Island was faintly silhouetted against the starlit arctic sky under a bright veil of northern lights, which stretched from horizon to horizon.

Along the coast of Ellesmere Island we could clearly distinguish the broad shelf ice, the glacial fringe, ten to twenty miles wide. At regular intervals our position was checked against three-star fixes. We passed the last reported position for T-1 near Ward Hunt Island, but saw no sign of it. Joe gave over the controls to Major Soderburg, and came aft to watch the radar scope. So far all had gone well, the engines were running smoothly, but our gas consumption was high.

On a normal mission the space in the navigation compartment is very crowded. Now with me there in addition to the usual crew it was almost impossible to move about without hitting one of the many vital instruments or bumping into one of the navigators making celestial observations through the astrodome. The atmosphere was tense as we were approaching the target. All eyes were on the radar scope, but no one said a word.

Suddenly the black contours of a triangular body moved in on the bright screen. As it slowly moved along toward the center of the scope, its size and shape identified it as T-1. A three-star fix was made, and the position determined to be eighty miles east of the last reported position.

We continued along the coast to examine the extent of the shelf ice until we could just make out Pearyland on the northern tip of Greenland. Here we turned back and made for base.

We had originally planned to proceed north and east from T-1 in search of T-2, which had moved only fifty miles south and west during the six months preceding August, 1951, when it was last seen. This plan had to be abandoned, however, for we had strong head winds, and the severe icing had reduced our ground speed by ten miles an hour, and our gas supply would not allow the necessary safety margin for this flight.

We landed in the middle of the night after an eighteen-hour flight and dropped in for a beer at the roadhouse on our way back to Fairbanks.

As the result of this mission, and after weighing all the hazards against the advantages, T-3 was now picked as our primary target.

From now on the project began to develop at a rate which at times was hard to keep up with. As soon as it became known that a landing on an ice island was to take place, scores of enthusiastic volunteers offered their services. The general interest in the project was such that it almost hampered the work, for all sorts of suggestions and ideas beyond the scope of the project poured in from all kinds of sources. At times, strange as it may seem, Joe had to make a considerable effort to dampen the excitement.

We soon realized that in view of the many unknown factors involved in the operation, it would be wise to proceed with caution, and decided, therefore, that the entire project should be carried out in three different stages.

The initial stage involved the preliminary exploratory phase of the project: the low-level reconnaissance and the initial landing with the establishment of a preliminary camp. From this camp surface reconnaissance would be carried out to determine the feasibility of setting up a permanent station on the ice island. This stage would be the most hazardous phase of the project. The second stage would consist of the actual building of a secure base with adequate permanent structures, electrical power, radio and a regular meteorological station. The third stage would concern the full scientific exploitation of the ice island as a base for detailed long-range scientific exploration of the Polar Basin.

The general plan for the initial phase of the project as we saw it at the time of planning included three possible alternatives: if we found that the surface was sufficiently smooth, the initial landing would be made by wheel landings with twin-engine C-47's and four-engine C-54's. Failing this, the second possibility involved a C-47 ski landing with the initial party who would prepare a strip for C-54 wheel landing, since C-54's are too large to be equipped with skis. In case conditions ruled out wheel landings altogether, only one possibility remained: the initial landing would be made with a ski-equipped C-47, bringing in the essential equipment and personnel, and the remaining supplies would be parachuted from C-54's.

Very little information about the actual surface of the island was available at that time; as I have said, practically all our knowledge was obtained from one or two aerial photographs taken by the 58th Squadron during some low passes. From the literature it appeared likely that we would encounter quite heavy winds and low temperatures, since Robert Peary reported temperatures down to −66° F. at the end of March in 1906, and frequently he had wind velocities up to gale force (thirty to sixty m.p.h.) in this area.

We expected that the sun would appear on the horizon somewhere between the 10th and the 13th of March. Prior to this date the lighting conditions would make landing difficult; there would be nothing more than a gray twilight without shadows or contrast. From the end of April, unfavorable weather with low clouds and fog could be expected, so that there was only a period of roughly thirty days in which to complete the initial phase of the project. Later on in the spring or early summer, when the melting started, probably from May or June, surface conditions for landings would be poor, and this state would probably last for some time. These factors had to be considered during the planning.

The plans were almost constantly being changed in accordance with the changing circumstances and instructions from higher headquarters. It should be borne in mind that because this was a military operation, decisions did not rest entirely with the leader, as is normally the case in arctic expeditions. However, by the end of January the plans began to take final shape.

While General Old desired a large group of men, at least fifteen persons, Joe insisted on a small group for the initial phase because of the requirements for support and for reasons of safety. After all, the fewer the people, the smaller the chances for casualties, and in case of catastrophe it is simpler to rescue a small body of men than a large one. Accordingly, a small group was recruited. Joe was assisted in administrative matters by Lieutenant R. R. Danner, of the 2107th Air Weather Group. The initial landing party was to consist of Lieutenant Colonel J. O. Fletcher, Captain M. F. Brinegar, on temporary duty with the 10th Air Rescue, Captain P. L. Green, the radio operator, and myself. Dr. A. P. Crary and R. Cotell, who had had previous experience in arctic operations on expeditions to the drift ice north of Alaska, arrived from the USAF Geophysical Laboratory at Cambridge, Massachusetts, and were to land as soon as conditions permitted. Their job would be to assist in the surface reconnnaissance and to start an extensive geophysical research program on the ice island, involving study of the bottom of the ocean, the ocean depth and its currents, the formation and the behavior of the sea ice, the origin and the characteristics of the ice island itself, and the pull of gravity of the earth at various locations.

The actual air operations were to be carried out by the 10th Air Rescue Squadron, Flight D, under Major G. F. Bradburn, who would be responsible for reconnaissance, landing, supply, and rescue operations. All navigational problems were handled by Captain E. F. Curley, of the 10th Air Rescue, with additional navigators supplied from the 58th Squadron.

Additional personnel, including scientists, weather observers and technicians, were to be sent out later on as soon as the station was established, providing it was found feasible to set up a permanent installation.

Thanks to the most excellent help and co-operation of everyone concerned, the supplies and equipment were gradually assembled as the hectic weeks went by.

On an expedition like this, minor discrepancies may well lead to fatal results. Joe, with his usual thoroughness, decided that we should unpack and try out every single item of the more essential equipment in a preliminary trial camp, which we established for this purpose on the frozen Chena River near Ladd Field. Here we erected the Jamesway huts which were to be our permanent shelters on T-3, completely equipped with stoves, beds and other furniture, cooking utensils, power generators, communications equipment, etc. For several weeks some of us actually lived in the camp, and discovered that we would need many items that we had overlooked during our initial planning. We also found faulty equipment which had to be replaced. For obvious reasons we wished to keep the general public away from the camp; this duty was assigned to Joe's dog, the Norwegian elkhound Tundra, who was to go along on the expedition as our mascot.

We realized from our previous experience when we had to live in the open in arctic Alaska that the standard sleeping bags and arctic clothing would not be adequate under the extreme conditions on T-3. To survive and to complete the initial operation successfully, proper protection against the killing cold and the blizzards was of vital importance, for severely frostbitten hands or feet could jeopardize the entire project by making hazardous rescue operation necessary. With this in mind, special all-down

sleeping bags were obtained, and extra windbreakers were added
to the equipment. In the limited time available for our preparations we failed to obtain special clothing of caribou skin, which
would have been just the thing to use on this expedition. It has
always been standard equipment for arctic explorers, but it
cannot be adopted as general issue for the Air Force, simply because not enough caribou skins can be obtained.

For the initial landing we brought one four-to-six-man double-
walled mountain tent and one wall-type fireproof tent. Of the
kinds available, these would give us the best shelters for the
amount of weight and space which could be allotted to tents.
In addition to the primus stoves, two sports heaters and one small
oil stove were included.

For the exploratory operations we brought special field rations
supplemented with various items of fresh food, and a thirty days'
supply of survival rations. The field rations were the so-called
5-in-1 rations which are conveniently packed in cases, each containing one day's rations for five men, or five days' rations for
one man, and consisting of different menus for breakfast, lunch
and dinner. They are easy to prepare, palatable, and have a high
nutritional value. Of the different field rations available we found
these were the closest to the type of diet we would normally
have at home, and they could therefore be used over a long period
of time without becoming monotonous. The fresh ration supple-
ments consisted mainly of some high-grade meat, bread, butter,
cheese, fruits, spices and sauces. As survival rations to be used
only in case of extreme emergency, we selected the latest Air
Force carbohydrate survival rations, both for reasons of weight
restrictions and because they could be eaten without previous
cooking. For the permanent camp, we laid in six thousand pounds
of regular messhall rations.

As much of the food and equipment as possible was packed in aluminum containers which could be parachuted from B-29 or from C-54 aircraft in case that turned out to be necessary.

As the supplies arrived at our warehouse, half a dozen experts set to work packing the precious goods, while the rest of us meticulously entered each single item on our lists as it was carefully wrapped and placed in the containers. When full the containers were strapped and sealed, and a code number was painted with bright luminous paint on the sides so that the numbers would be clearly visible when the containers were landed in the snow. Then they were weighed and loaded on trucks and taken to one of the 10th Air Rescue Squadron hangars where they were stacked along the wall according to priority, ready for loading into the aircraft at short notice. During the crating we had remarkably few accidents, but once a sack of peas broke, so that a line of peas marked the route of the truck from our warehouse to the hangar.

This job, however monotonous, was important; none of us would care to try to find a box of matches among two hundred cases without knowing which one to open.

In a special shed the individual survival gear was being packed into rucksacks. Each member was to carry his own so that the essential clothing, bedding, tools, fuel, stoves and rations, etc., would be at hand in case of a crash landing or a bail-out on the ice.

On February 27, the first 27,000 pounds of equipment and rations were flown to Thule, Northwest Greenland. With it went Joe and other project personnel who made the necessary arrangements for hangar space and maintenance facilities for our aircraft, storage space for our 75,000 pounds of supplies, and billeting and mess facilities for the large number of people engaged in the project. They also made the necessary co-ordinations with the Northeast Air Command for the future large-scale T-3 operations which were to take place from this staging base, the major American air base nearest to T-3.

CHAPTER TEN

Across the Canadian Archipelago
to Thule

By the beginning of March the preparations for the adventure had reached a climax. Supplies were still pouring in and were filling our warehouse. Additional items of equipment which were ordered at the last minute were rushed through supply channels at high priority. We had reached a point where we were all working like mad to tie up the odd ends which had been left to the last. There was no longer time to order any further equipment, and we could only hope that what we already had would be all that we needed.

My own personal preparations were fairly simple, for during my stay in Alaska I had been going on field trips all the time. I only had to pull out my old arctic clothing, which had passed the test on previous expeditions. For the last time I went through my medical bag to make certain that all the items were there, and that it contained no solutions that might freeze. In my rucksack I added an extra set of underclothes, some socks, and a few survival rations which might come in handy in an emergency. When, in addition, I had checked my skis and snowshoes, I was prepared to leave at any time; in fact, I felt the sooner the better. We had had more than enough of packing and hauling heavy cases about during the last hectic weeks; now we were raring to go.

Monday, March 10, we were at last ready to move from Ladd A.F.B., Alaska, with the three aircraft carrying all our equipment, the project personnel, the air crews, additional technicians and maintenance personnel, totaling approximately forty people.

We were briefed in the 10th Rescue hangar in the morning, prior to take-off. It was a keen group that gathered in front of the large map of the North Polar Basin to hear Major Bradburn sum up the purpose and the scope of the mission. He outlined the schedule for the flight across the frigid Canadian Archipelago to Thule. Then followed various technical details, how much load we would carry, quantities of gas, and what we should do in case of trouble. Toward the end of the briefing we were suddenly disturbed by a message from the weather officer predicting very bad weather along our route. The start had to be postponed twenty-four hours.

We were so anxious to get going that this disappointment was probably as hard felt as any setback we encountered during the entire project. However, these extra twenty-four hours gave us a chance to wind up all sorts of odd jobs which would otherwise have been left to those who remained behind.

The delay also gave me an unexpected opportunity to spend some peaceful hours at home with my wife, which had rarely been possible in the past hectic weeks. I was also able to have lunch with my good friend Dr. Paul Haggland in whose very capable hands I had left the business of delivering our expected baby.

The following day, March 11, was ideal, with bright sun and clear weather along the entire route. There was tremendous activity and a feeling of excitement around the hangars, and at three o'clock in the afternoon we watched our ski-equipped C-47 take off from Ladd A.F.B. to fly to Barter Island on the north coast of Alaska, where it was to refuel and wait for the two escorting C-54's. As it circled the field and headed northward toward the Brooks Range I had a strange feeling of satisfaction.

In the evening we gathered with all our personal gear and individual survival equipment at the hangar. The loading of the two C-54's was in full swing; the flight line was humming with activity in the bright moonlight; the navigators were sorting out their maps. There was no doubt that now we were off at last.

We were told to get aboard the leading radar-equipped C-54, piloted by Captain E. G. Smith. At ten o'clock we took to the air on schedule and set course for Barter Island. As we flew in over Barter Island, the C-47 lifted from the ground to follow us across the Canadian Archipelago to Thule. At the same time the second C-54 under Major Bradburn took off from Ladd to follow in our wake.

And so the flight went on, uneventfully, through the starlit arctic night, across the Canadian Arctic, over mountains where glaciers twisted down between the windblown snow-covered peaks, pouring into the bay ice like frosting on a cake.

Stretched out on the floor and on the benches were the project personnel, twenty-four men in all: the landing party, a para-doctor team, all the aircraft engineers, the ground crews and personal equipment personnel. Joe's dog, Tundra, wandered about unhappy and restless. Some of the crew started to play cards but soon had to give up, for it became so cold in the plane that they had enough to do trying to keep themselves warm. The rest of us tried in vain to sleep, but were prevented by the cold, and spent the hours with chattering teeth. Even so we felt happy and relieved, as one always does when an expedition is finally under way.

The C-47, slowed down by the skis under its belly, could by no

means keep up with us, and as the hours passed, the distance
between us became greater. Behind it and gradually catching
up with it came the second C-54, with several thousand pounds
of cargo on board, including the rest of our survival gear and
three hundred pounds of dynamite for the seismographic measurements of the depth of the Polar Sea.

Over Ellesmere Island the moon vanished and the day dawned
ahead. Below us we could barely see the shimmering landscape
of snow and ice. Then came Smith Sound, covered with cracked
drift ice and icebound bergs, and beyond it Greenland rose from
the sea.

It was three o'clock in the afternoon, March 12, when we
touched down on the snow-covered runway at Thule. While we
were still standing in the bitter cold in front of the operations
hut Major Bradburn's C-54 came in and landed on three engines.
As he taxied up toward the flight line, the C-47 appeared in the
sky, circled the field, and Captain Lew Erhart put her gently
down on the ground. Soon the three aircraft were lined up side
by side; the first step of the operation was successfully accomplished without a hitch. This was a good start, and the occasion
called for a brief celebration before we went on to tackle the
second phase.

Close to Thule, this new American stronghold on the fringe of
the frozen north at the end of the world, lies the Eskimo colony
established by the Danish explorer, Knud Rasmussen, in 1910.
The Americans may claim an interest in this remote corner of the
world for more reasons than one, for here they are on traditional
ground. Through many years this was the regular stamping
ground of Peary. The story is that Rasmussen quickly organized
the colony when he learned of Peary's intention to establish a
trading post at Thule. They say that when Peary arrived the

following year and saw the Danish flag flying above the colony, he lost his temper, failed to watch his course and ran the ship aground.

The colony was organized on a purely private basis, and has proved a most successful enterprise. Today the population consists of about 350 Eskimos. A handful of Danes of the local Greenland administration are housed in the vicinity of the native settlement.

The Eskimos at Thule are in several respects different from the rest of the natives of Greenland, and have remained more untouched by civilization. While the natives further south insist on being called Greenlanders, those of Thule refer to themselves as Eskimos. They are proud and independent and have maintained a higher state of economy, owing to the abundance of game and fur-bearing animals in the district. They are, therefore, reluctant to engage themselves as servants for the whites. In their pride they are easily offended; the slightest unpleasant remark is often enough to cause the Thule Eskimo to get up and leave.

In the afternoon the director of the Danish radio station, Leo Christiansen, whom I had last seen twelve years earlier when we traveled together by dog team on the east coast of Greenland, took me over to the Eskimo village in his jeep to find out if we could obtain some fur clothing for the expedition.

This gave me a most welcome opportunity to visit the Thule Eskimos. I had heard much about them but I had never before had an occasion to go to Thule.

We approached the settlement from the sea, driving across the fjord ice between the icebergs locked in the bay. The Danish colony consisted of a dozen red and green painted houses centered around the church and a hospital on the slope by the fjord. Huge white and yellow Thule huskies were chained in front of every house, and by the shore ice a group of young Eskimo boys in furry polar bear skin trousers were practicing with whips of the characteristic Thule design: a thin skin rope of bearded seal fixed to a handle of driftwood. Pretty Eskimo women in long white skin boots called kamiks, worn outside socks of hareskin, walked stiff-legged between the houses carrying their babies inside their parkas of doghide, the little black-eyed faces peeping out from under the hoods. These Eskimos no longer wear only their picturesque native costumes, but purchase most of their garments through the American mail-order catalogues. Old men standing by the main store, their black shining hair cut straight across their foreheads, puffed contentedly on their pipes and grinned as we passed them.

At this outpost of civilization the isolated community of a handful of Danish officials endure the extremes of the arctic elements. At the end of October the sun sets for the winter, not to appear again in the sky until the beginning of February. On the wall in the radio station there is a dial showing the one hundred dark, sunless days, and for each day that passes the hand is moved forward one degree across the face of the dial.

The winter darkness is the central problem of this society, the effect of which no one escapes. It is the topic everyone talks about; the arctic twilight, followed by the gray and finally the black darkness that prevails day and night, is the dreaded event by the coming of fall.

Christiansen's little green house was surrounded by a fence to protect his children against attack by the savage husky dogs. We were talking of the dark period as we pulled up in front. "It is terrible," he said. "In the winter the children cannot get out to play in the fresh air for days on end. It is a life for men, but not for women or children."

Beyond the hillcrest of windblown snow and gravel, less than a mile away from the Danish colony, lies the Eskimo settlement: igloos of driftwood and snow-covered sod and stones on the slope between the colorful mountains, overlooking the Polar Sea and the islands. The sun stood low over the frozen sea, still shining on the mountain walls and the edge of the Greenland Ice Cap behind the village. Turned-over kayaks were lying on racks by the beach where sled tracks wound in among the icebergs.

The Danish physician Dr. Johansen drove us over to the Eskimo village with his dog team. At first the settlement appeared lifeless. The smoke curling from the chimneys whirled straight up into the clear frosty sky. The physician explained that the deserted appearance of the village was due to the fact that these Eskimos sleep most of the day when they are not hunting. The Eskimo dogs lazily raised their heads as we drove by. Then Eskimo faces which all looked alike began to appear from behind the little igloos; one by one the girls came out through the driftwood doors to see who was coming. The women eventually gathered in the shadows of the houses to watch, and the children collected wood and blubber from the racks and disappeared through the low narrow tunnel which leads into the main room of the house where the hunters were taking a nap around the stove in the center.

The main diet of these people is the meat and organs of seal and walrus, and occasionally narwhale and polar bear. They eat the meat raw or boiled, and a particular delicacy is the seasoned meat of auklets, kept uncleaned with blubber in sealskin bags for several months.

One of the houses looked different from the rest. It was built of an abandoned American glider plane which had blown off on the ice and been salvaged by the Eskimo, who tugged it to the village by his dogs. Here a baby boy had just been born as we arrived, and the Eskimo midwife looked pleased as she grinned at us through the door.

A seventy-five-year-old man came across the hillcrest poking his stick in the gravel as he walked almost noiselessly on his bearskin kamiks. He wore trousers and a parka of bearskin. This was Ootah, who marched with Peary to the Pole in 1909. He is very popular among his relatives, for he receives a regular American pension in recognition of his previous service with Peary.

A team of a dozen galloping dogs harnessed in fan formation turned in on the shore ice from the bay, with a boy sitting on a load of meat on the sledge. He had come from the walrus hunt miles out on the fjord close to the edge of the bay ice, where the hunters had been harpooning walrus at the breathing holes for several days. This can be a dangerous game, for the walrus is not always the loser. As the animal rises through the hole in the ice the Eskimo thrusts his harpoon into its flesh. To the head of the harpoon is fastened a skin rope to prevent the animal from sinking. An Eskimo told me that he once saw a hunter caught in the rope and pulled under the ice as the wounded walrus dived.

To the Eskimo, dog driving and hunting are not considered work, but sports which they all thoroughly enjoy. They are never in a hurry; they take life easy, sleep a lot and are apparently happy.

At the time of our visit there was a serious shortage of polar bear and caribou skins in the village. The polar bear hunt that year had so far been exceptionally poor, and the supply of caribou skins was already exhausted. These skins have to be imported by the trading post every summer since the caribou are no longer obtainable locally. We were therefore unable to procure any suitable Eskimo fur garments for the expedition, and returned to the base with our purpose unaccomplished.

In the evening the staff of the Thule Air Base were briefed on the plans for the Icicle Project. Joe outlined the historical background and the over-all purpose of the project, and Major Bradburn summarized the plans for the actual air operations. When we told them what we would need in the way of assistance and support from them they showed the greatest willingness to co-operate.

Following this general briefing, discussions continued between the various technical groups regarding communication procedures, transportation, the supply of fuel and oil, etc., until late in the night, when all major problems had been settled in principle.

Up to this time, the exact location of T-3 was unknown. On March 8 and again on March 12 the 58th Reconnaissance Squadron had flown a "Ptarmigan" mission to the North Pole with the idea of locating T-3. They were forced to return at eighty degrees or about five hundred miles short of the estimated position of T-3 on both occasions, however, so that recent information on the exact position of T-3 was still lacking.

In order to get ahead with the project, the first thing we had to do was to locate T-3. We therefore decided to make a special reconnaissance flight by four-engined C-54 to pinpoint the island. This mission was set up for the 14th of March. We planned to carry fuel for sixteen hours' flying, and if all went well we hoped to have a chance to look for T-2 north of Greenland on our return.

CHAPTER ELEVEN

Striking North

We took off on the special reconnaissance mission to T-3 on the evening of March 14 with four pilots, five navigators and the initial landing party, in order that we might all have a chance to get acquainted with the surface characteristics of the ice island—if we succeeded in finding it. The time of the take-off was arranged to avoid as much of the period of twilight as possible.

It darkened as we flew to the north until we passed Alert on the north coast of Ellesmere Island when it again began to brighten, with a reddening in the sky ahead toward the Pole. At midnight we reached the Pole, turned left and followed the 180th meridian toward Alaska.

The weather was fine, with excellent visibility, so that our chances of finding T-3 were the very best, especially since the radar functioned exceptionally well that day. Nevertheless there was a noticeable feeling of tension among us, for the future of the project depended greatly on the results of this mission. Joe was standing next to the radar operator, who never for a moment removed his eyes from the screen, on which the radar return sketched the ever-changing picture of irregular pack ice and a criss-cross of narrow fissures between the floes. The rest of us

154

watched them anxiously from the cabin door, or peered through the frosty fuselage windows for signs of the target.

About thirty minutes after we passed the Pole the radar observer noticed on the screen an object resembling T-3 thirty miles to our left, but we flew on to the last known position of the island—87° 44′ N., 180° W. At this point we turned back and flew due north parallel to our previous route toward the object seen in the radar scope. Then, suddenly, at 1:15 A.M., we flew in over T-3, floating like a huge aircraft carrier amidst the pack ice, at 88° 17′ N., 166° 30′ W., a position much further north than earlier reported.

Major Bradburn immediately let down to an altitude of one hundred feet. At the same time we removed the drop door at the side of the fuselage, to have a good look at the island that had been the center of our thoughts for many weeks, and which in all probability would be our camping ground in a not-too-distant future. Joe hurried to place a ladder across the door to prevent the eager observers from falling out of the aircraft, which during the low passes was bouncing along through the bumpy air close to the surface.

I was lying flat on the floor next to Joe and Mike Brinegar, while Lew Erhart and some of the navigators leaned forward above us. We had to hold on to our arctic helmets to keep them from being sucked out through the door by the slipstream, which almost took our breaths away as we pressed forward as far as we could in order to see as much as possible.

What we saw was exactly what the photographs had led us to expect: a vast white flat field surrounded by tight pack ice with only narrow fissures and frozen leads between the floes. It was approximately five by nine miles in size, judging by the time it took to fly across it at a known speed; in shape, it was oblong with rounded corners, and slightly elevated in the center. From the air, in the dim light, clear blue ice seemed to shine through the snow in several places on the highest ridges.

It is true that this tabular berg really does not look like an island in the usual sense of the word. However, it stands out distinctly among the surrounding pack ice—a huge sturdy body of ice entirely different from the regular sea ice. As I looked down on it I felt thoroughly at home, for I could almost identify each ridge and trough from the oft-studied pictures.

When I had seen all I wanted to I withdrew from the door to allow some of the others to have a closer look.

The pilots were all convinced that a C-47 ski landing would present no difficulty. "It's a cinch," said Lew Erhart as he gave me a whack on the shoulder. "We'll ride her right in!"

The surface looked fairly even, although its appearance varied from one place to another. The snow seemed to be hard packed, but from the air we couldn't determine the exact depth. The question of a wheels-down C-54 landing was, therefore, still unsettled; it could only be decided from the ground.

We headed for our home base. For more than four hours we flew through the twilight, without any stars or sun and with the gyro compass as our only aid in navigation. We landed, chilled to the bone, after twelve and a half hours' flying.

After a meal and a shower we gathered in our quarters for a beer while we discussed the results of the mission. On the basis of our findings everyone seemed optimistic about the suitability of T-3 for a base and the prospects for a successful landing. T-3 was therefore definitely to remain our final target. As this question was settled once and for all, we were now ready for the next step, the actual landing.

Major Bradburn turned to the navigators and asked them to

work out the earliest possible date for the initial landing on the basis of the twilight situation. Captain Curley pulled out his handbooks and tables from under the bed and started some complicated figuring. He came out with the answer: Thursday, March 20. This was accepted as our D-day.

Next we had to select a suitable advanced refueling point for the C-47, for the distance from Thule to T-3 was at that time over 850 nautical miles, and the round trip—over 1,700 miles—was too long to allow any margin of safety. Under the circumstances we either had to establish a fuel cache on the drift ice, or to stage from T-1. In case we should decide to use T-1 as a refueling base, we considered landing a C-47 with eight drums of fuel on March 17 and making a second flight on March 18 with the geophysicist Dr. Crary and his assistant, who would remain on T-1 until after the initial landing on T-3.

The advantage of this alternative was that we could apparently always count on being able to land on T-1, weather permitting; and the fuel cache would be safe, while on the pack ice it might be lost if the ice broke up. In addition, this plan would permit Dr. Crary to examine the characteristics of T-1 while waiting for the initial camp to be established on T-3, thus greatly adding to the scientific results of the expedition.

After lengthy discussions it was decided to send out a C-47 with a minimum crew under Captain Lew Erhart to establish a fuel cache on T-1. If the limited navigational aids carried by the C-47 prevented them from finding T-1, they were to establish the cache on a frozen lead in the pack ice, preferably somewhere between Greenland and Ellesmere Island, as far north as practical.

This plan involved several risks. A landing on T-1 would be the first landing ever made on an ice island, and we knew little of its surface characteristics, possible cracks and old drainage

systems. The ski take-off with a maximum load from a snow surface might well be critical. Because of the pay load, only the
very minimum of survival gear and rations could be carried.
Navigation through the zone of twilight without radar would
undoubtedly be difficult, and they might have trouble in finding
the ice island, which would mean a loss of time and fuel. The
fuel amount would in any case be drastically small, and the
situation would become even more critical if fuel consumption
were to be increased by ski friction, head winds, prolonged taxiing, or unfavorable weather on the return journey.

On Monday, March 17, when Captain Erhart took off at
8:00 A.M. in the ski-equipped C-47 the weather was clear with
sun, but it was cold at Thule, and further north the weather
report gave one mile visibility with snow. Erhart's last report
came at 11:00 A.M. when he gave his position as only fifteen
miles west of his position at ten-thirty. Following this he remained silent. For two hours we stood around the radio operators
anxiously listening for his signals while we speculated about the
reason for his silence. Perhaps they were flying in circles looking
for a hole in the undercast, or perhaps they had lost radio contact, or perhaps they had landed on the ice and were stuck.

Finally, after hours of tense anxiety, we again established contact with the C-47, but it was not until they landed at 4:30 P.M.
that we received the complete story. They had flown northward
against strong head winds and low visibility; then they lost radio
contact and flew for five hours in search of T-1, but had to give
up because of the weather. They eventually landed on six feet
of ice in a frozen lead between old floes, at 82° 30′ N., 60° W.
between Ellesmere Island and Greenland. Everywhere in the
vicinity the ice was tightly packed with only very small cracks
across the landing strip. They spent half an hour on the ice, leav-

ing six drums of gas in a row; the remaining two drums they used during their return journey.

Now that the gas cache was established, there was nothing to prevent us from going ahead with the project.

The following day, Tuesday, March 18, while we were busy loading the three aircraft for the final operation, General Old arrived from Alaska. As he stepped out of his C-54, loaded with six thousand pounds of additional equipment, including furniture for the permanent base, he asked Joe and Major Bradburn how things were going. They reported our plans for the initial landing on Thursday, March 20.

"Why not tomorrow?" asked the General.

It turned out that the U.S. Navy had just released the news that they were on their way to T-3. They had announced that Navy fliers had started from Point Barrow on Monday, March 17, to establish two depots on the drift ice as staging bases for their northward dash. This came as a complete surprise to us, for we had been informed that they would go ahead with their scientific program in the drift ice north of Alaska during March, and would eventually land on T-3 as a link in this program after we had established the base during the latter half of the month.

"If the Navy can fly over the central Polar Basin on March 19, I can see no reason why the Air Force should not be capable of doing the same thing," argued the General. "Perhaps we would land simultaneously on T-3."

It was decided to step up the plan and to make our initial landing on Wednesday, March 19, and to include the third C-54 in the flight.

Joe came over to the warehouse to tell us about the General's decision. Lieutenant Danner and I were frantically trying to reduce the load of bare essentials for the initial landing party from

3,700 to 1,200 pounds, which was the absolute maximum weight which could be carried in the C-47 with the full gas load and the large fuselage tank, in addition to the crew and the landing party of four. With the step-up in plans there was no time for lengthy discussions, so we solved the problem by preparing the rest of the equipment for parachuting from one of the C-54's. This would give us all we would need for survival on T-3, even if it should prove impossible for the C-54's to land. At this stage of the project, however, we still felt fairly hopeful about the prospects for C-54 wheel landings.

The final briefing was held in the evening, and all of us felt the drama of the occasion. The C-47 would take off at 8:00 A.M. and would land at the fuel cache three hours later. The refueling would be completed in one hour. The three C-54's would take off from Thule at one-hour intervals and the leading C-54 would rendezvous with the C-47 over the cache at noon. The four aircraft would then fly on to T-3, arriving at the end of three hours, so that the landing could be made in maximum daylight. A period of three hours was allotted for the activities over or on T-3, and during the return flight only one hour twilight would be encountered. The four aircraft would land at Thule in the night. General Old was to go along as co-pilot in the C-47. Captain Green, our radio operator on the landing party, would go with the main radio equipment in one of the C-54's, and the *Life* photographer, Mr. George Silk, would take his place in the C-47. No one had shown greater enthusiasm or had worked harder than Captain Green throughout all the weeks of preparation, and he had been looking forward to being among the first to land on the untrodden island of ice; yet he betrayed no sign of disappointment and went to his work as keen as ever.

General Old ended the briefing by pointing out that if all went well, and if every man did his duty as well as in the past weeks of preparation, the United States Air Force would have a station on T-3 within the next twenty-four hours.

However, all our troubles were not yet over. Later in the evening as we went down to the hangars to help load the last of the equipment and to put the parachutes on the dropping containers, we were told that the only available radar on the leading C-54 was out of order. This was a serious blow, for it was obvious that without radar and by visual observation alone it would be futile to attempt to locate the target.

Captain Green and his crew worked on the radar all night without a stop, but in vain. At five-thirty as my alarm clock went off, Major Bradburn put his head through the door and told me to go back to sleep, for the operation was postponed since the radar was still out of order. At first I thought he was joking, but when I finally realized that he was deadly serious, I went back to bed. Little more than an hour later, there was another violent bang on the door. "Hurry up! We're going after all," shouted Brad, and before I had time to question him he was gone.

I stumbled to my feet and went out into the washroom to find the crews tumbling about half awake in utter confusion. Eventually we learned what had happened. When Captain Green reported to Joe and Brad at daybreak that the radar could not be repaired, they decided unanimously to postpone the operation. They immediately reported to the General, who was already eating his preflight breakfast in the messhall, and explained that they had been compelled to postpone the flight because of the faulty radar.

"Radar or no radar," said the General, "let's go."

Brad then rushed back to our quarters with his orders: "The General says go, so we go!"

We lost no time in getting ready. It had always been my

practice when about to set out on an arctic journey to eat as if each meal were the last one. On this occasion time did not permit me to observe my rule.

There was only one thought in everyone's mind—to get aboard the airplane in time. Bags, flying clothing, cameras, binoculars and other items of equipment were tossed out into the hallway. There was no time to wait for a truck, so we loaded ourselves with as much as we could carry and set out for the aerodrome.

As we came staggering along with our gear to operations the aircraft were already lined up by the flight line ready to fly.

It was not until all our gear was aboard that we had time to relax for a moment while we waited for the photographers to take their pictures. Our friends had gathered around to say good-by and to wish us good luck. By now we began to feel that we were embarking upon a historical flight, full of hazards, dangers and exciting adventure. This was our D-day—the day we had looked forward to for so long.

Ten minutes behind schedule we were airborne, our engines tracing two solitary vapor trails across the pale sky toward the Pole.

As we were flying northward across the pack ice I noticed to my great concern that the ice had broken up in the strait between Greenland and Ellesmere Island since the gas cache had been dumped there two days earlier. As far as I could see to the north there was much open water, and icebergs and loose pack ice had started to move southward with the swift current.

With a feeling of growing anxiety I realized that the frozen lead in the sea ice where the six fuel drums had been left could well have broken up. If that had happened we would be unable to land and the drums would be at the bottom of the sea. Even under the best circumstances, it is no easy task to locate a fuel

drum in the middle of the arctic pack ice. It is like looking for a
needle in a haystack.

"What will we do if we can't find the gas cache?" I asked Lew
Erhart as he came aft to check the right engine, which had developed a slight oil leak.

He grinned and shrugged his shoulders as he always does
when things are tough. "Cut the mixture lean and keep on going,"
he said.

Erhart is a remarkable man. He can look so incredibly care-
free and unaffected when he is in a tight spot. He has made more
landings on the pack ice than any other pilot I have known. With
him I would have no hesitation in going anywhere at any time,
for I have confidence in his judgment and abilities. This I cannot
say about all the pilots in whose hands I have placed my life in
the Arctic.

We flew across much open water, scattered pack ice and floating icebergs. As we went on, however, and approached the part
of the strait where the gap between Greenland and Ellesmere
Island is so narrow that on a clear day you can see across from
one coast to another, the ice became more packed and was intact
from coast to coast.

We were nearing 82° 30′ N., the site of the fuel cache. Now,
if we could only detect the drums in the snow, in the middle of
this white expanse of frozen sea. . . .

Through the starboard blister window I suddenly saw a row of
six tiny black spots in the snow to the right, at the end of a long
frozen lead. At the same moment the aircraft banked and started
down to make the landing. We huddled together on the floor with
our backs against the wall in order to get the weight as far forward as possible.

Erhart made a low pass, and came in for a wheels-down landing. He dropped the flaps, touched down and landed the heavy aircraft gently on the frozen lead, coming to a complete stop in front of the drums. This was at 11:50 A.M.

As we opened the door and jumped out on the ice, a biting breeze nipped us in the face. It was about −60° F., and the pale sun shone through the frosty haze. We were standing on a frozen lead four thousand feet long and three hundred feet broad, covered with less than an inch of snow. In the distance we could see the snow-clad mountains of Greenland beyond the pack ice to the east, and the cliffs of Ellesmere to the west. It was here that the Greenland Eskimos through centuries used to cross from Greenland to Ellesmere Island to hunt polar bears and musk oxen in the spring. Under favorable conditions the journey could be made in a matter of hours, but once in a great while they were caught in a storm while still in the strait, and were carried with the ice into the ocean.

It was also at this point that Robert Peary staggered across from Greenland back to his base on Ellesmere Island in 1906.

General Old and Joe were the first to reach the fuel drums, and began to roll them across the ice. The engineer started the pump and began to fuel the aircraft, while the movie camera kept buzzing until it froze in the cold, and the photographer returned to the ship with rime frost in his fur, and slightly frost-bitten fingers.

The refueling was completed at 12:20 P.M., when we again climbed into the aircraft and the engines were started. The left engine hesitated for a moment, but soon the ship moved slowly toward the end of the lead. Erhart brought her into position, made a final check of the engines while the rest of us pressed our backs against the wall and looked at each other. This was the moment we had feared, a take-off with the overloaded aircraft from the pack ice.

We braced our backs against the wall and stemmed our feet against the fuel tank. As we raced along the ice under the roar of the engines, the seconds became hours as hummocks flew by the windows; then we felt a jerk, and we started to rise.

When the power was reduced to cruising speed and we were heading toward 88° 17′ N., 166° 30′ W., the General came aft to stretch his legs. He smiled as he said: "Thank God that's over with."

No doubt the General had every reason to feel relieved, for the landing and take-off of heavy aircraft on floating sea ice are still among the unusual and rather hazardous types of Air Force operations.

Generally speaking, the largest unbroken ice floes are found in the regions close to the center of the Polar Basin. Here they are usually covered with only a comparatively thin layer of snow, and thus are best for aircraft operations.

As yet data on the thickness of ice necessary to support aircraft landings are incomplete. The ice must be strong enough to withstand the impact of the aircraft at the moment of landing at the point where the landing gear hits the ice. Since the ice is not perfectly elastic, pressure over a period of several hours may produce substantial sagging. Therefore, though the ice may be strong enough to support a landing, it may sag and break when the aircraft is left standing. During landing, the shock of the impact is to a great extent transferred to the underlying water upon which the ice rests. As a rule, ice thicker than thirty-six inches is sufficient to support a C-47 landing, while a C-54 may require as much as fifty inches.

To land on sea ice a pilot needs to be experienced in judging the ice from the air. From its color and general appearance he must be able to estimate its thickness and strength, and he must be able to detect obscure obstacles and other traps.

But the greatest danger to the polar flier is the "white out," when there is a slight haze or overcast, and the sky and the white surface of the snow fuse together so that there is no horizon, and no shadows or objects to aid the flier's depth perception. Under these conditions of universal whitening, the pilot flying contact is unable to tell how far he is off the ground, so that he may proceed to make the landing ten or fifty feet up in the air— or while in level flight he may suddenly discover that he has landed.

The engines hummed monotonously as we flew on northward at an altitude of one thousand feet. The two coasts merged together underneath us, then they diverged again, and at one o'clock in the afternoon we left the north coast of Ellesmere Island behind us and headed north across the plains of polar pack ice toward the Pole.

At this point I caught a glimpse of the rugged mountains of Pearyland as they vanished behind the horizon to the east. This is the northernmost country in the world, its northern shores being little more than six degrees of latitude from the North Pole itself. It was first seen by Robert Peary from Navy Cliff on the 4th of July, 1892, at the end of a seven-hundred-mile sled journey across the Ice Cap from the west coast of Greenland.

The interior of Pearyland was explored in detail during the Danish Pearyland Expedition in 1947-1950, the purpose of which was to set up a station, established and maintained by air, to investigate the comparatively unknown regions north of Independence Fjord. Before that time several expeditions had failed to reach this inaccessible region, which prior to the use of aircraft could only be approached across the Ice Cap from the west, or along five hundred miles of mountainous coastline and pack ice impossible to navigate by ship.

In July, 1947, during the first exploratory phase of the Danish Pearyland Expedition, in which I took part as the biologist and physician, we landed with a Catalina flying boat on the ice-free Brönlundfjord, latitude 82° N., and established a tent camp for the summer. Our aircraft crashed into the sea during the landing at our southern staging base in Northeast Greenland, and for seventeen days we were stranded in the interior of Pearyland until we were finally rescued by plane in the face of the approaching winter.

During the expedition we found that Pearyland is a desert of sand and stones from the coast to the mountains. It is free of ice except for a small area in the interior, but once it was totally glaciated like the rest of Greenland. The climate is dry like that of a desert, with tremendous sandstorms which have polished the stones and killed the vegetation, except in sheltered oases where we found a luxuriant vegetation and an abundance of game: musk oxen by the hundreds, swarms of hares, foxes, and flocks of ptarmigan. We discovered the remnants of Eskimo dwellings and utensils, which they had abandoned in the sand during their eastward migration several hundred years ago.

Recently the United States and Denmark have established another joint weather station at this end of the world as a further link in their growing chain of outposts along the entrance to the Polar Basin.

CHAPTER TWELVE

We Land on an Island of Ice

As we headed north from the land, above the interminable desert of ice, the fuselage tank still contained almost four hundred gallons of gas, but the gas gauge was frozen, so the engineer had to check the fuel with the aid of a stick.

Joe served as radio operator during the flight, for the crew had been cut to the absolute minimum to save weight. He had maintained contact with the escorting ships, and learned that the second and third C-54's had had minor engine trouble and some difficulty in taking off.

Mike Brinegar, who also was a member of our landing party, gave Captain Curley a hand with the navigation. Captain Curley, crack navigator of the 10th Air Rescue Squadron, was chosen for this job because of his extensive experience in polar navigation. In the crowded navigation compartment of our C-47 the two men worked constantly. While one of them at short intervals climbed up on a ration case to take sun shots through the astrodome, the other would check our drift by observing the ice through a sight in the floor.

Polar navigation is a science of its own. Where we were flying the ordinary magnetic compass was of no help, for the compass needle, instead of pointing north toward the geographical North Pole, as it does at more southern latitudes, pointed in the opposite direction, because the magnetic North Pole which attracts the needle is located in the middle of the Canadian Arctic Archipelago, which was south of our position. The radio compass was of no use either, for there was no radio beam to follow in this uninhabited desert of ice. Even the gyro compass, although it is not affected by magnetism, is for some reason not one hundred per cent trustworthy at these latitudes, and polar navigators of long standing have told me of strange incidents where the gyro fooled them into flying in circles. There are no landmarks whatever, nothing but white ice and the empty space over it from horizon to horizon.

The only reliable aids in navigation under these circumstances are the sun and the stars, but astronavigation is possible only when the stars are visible at night, or the sun in the day. In between there is the long period of twilight when it is neither day nor night, when the sun is below the horizon, but it is still too light for the stars to be visible.

This period of twilight used to be the nightmare of polar navigators, and at this particular time of the year it lasts for many hours. Our mission was planned so that we would encounter a minimum of twilight during the flight, and yet we would arrive over the target at maximum daylight. This is why the navigator had the final say when the time of take-off was selected, and during the actual flight it was the navigator who controlled the ship. At regular intervals, he plotted our position by sun shots and from time to time gave new readings to the pilot.

During the first part of the flight we had a thirty-mile head wind, but since we had left the coast it had died down to fifteen miles per hour. Our gas consumption was low, so all looked well, although Erhart had cut the gas mixture so lean that the engines sputtered and coughed once in a while and caused some concern among those of us who were not too familiar with the technicalities. One of our party, for instance, sincerely believed that the engines were about to quit, so he buckled on his parachute harness and hurried to the door as if to jump, but refrained when he stopped to realize that he would be no safer down on the ice.

So far the weather was excellent, with a clear sky, brilliant sunshine and good visibility. We maintained an altitude of one thousand feet; the lifeless pack ice swept by as the hours passed, with no signs of life in any form. Here and there I imagined I saw black specks which resembled seals, but a closer examination invariably revealed them to be merely shadows in the snow from the hummocks.

As we flew on northward across the ice, we passed the hours in shivering silence. My mind was occupied with thoughts of what to do in case we were forced down on the ice, our chances of survival, of being found in the middle of three million square miles of ice, and I tried to visualize the problems that we would encounter when we were left on T-3.

Because of the weight distribution in the aircraft we had been warned against making it tail-heavy by moving toward the rear of the ship. The large fuselage tank took up most of the space forward, and the seats were all occupied by bulky equipment which was securely strapped down and could not be removed. This left us only a tiny space by the wall separating the navigation compartment from the fuselage, where we could hardly move about at all. Once in a while, we had a chance to warm up, one at a time, by standing in the cabin behind the pilots, until we got in the way of the navigators when they had to make another sun shot through the astrodome.

Curley had figured on a three to four hour flight from the coast of Ellesmere Island to T-3, depending on the weather. The weather of course was the great unknown factor, on account of the lack of information on the huge uninhabited area around the Pole. Consequently the weather forecasts could only be approximate and based to a great extent on speculation. In the far North the weather is highly unpredictable anyhow; gales may spring up without a warning and whip the snow into blinding blizzards in a matter of minutes. The wind may change direction and rotate in a complete 360-degree circle in less than an hour, and several different low-pressure centers may be encountered between the mainland and the Pole during a single flight. Generally speaking, the flying weather is good in the winter, when navigation is also safest because of the abundance of stars for astronavigation; but ice landings or activities requiring visual observation at this time of the year are prohibited because of the darkness. During the summer, on the other hand, there is almost constantly a heavy overcast from the time the leads begin to occur in the pack ice, and the treacherous milky haze is one of the greatest dangers of all.

Colonel John Conrad of the 2107th Weather Group had made a special effort to provide weather forecasts for our area of operations, based to a great extent on information gathered by the 58th Weather Squadron during their regular weather missions to the Pole. This service proved most excellent, and made our job much easier.

So far we had been flying entirely according to directions from Curley. During the initial part of the flight he had had excellent and reliable sun shots and good visibility for determining the drift. By four o'clock in the afternoon, however, the visibility had dwindled to less than a mile; the sun was low on the horizon and looked like a flat oval disk. Then it disappeared entirely behind the clouds. The ice was covered by a thin haze, and there was no horizon.

By this time we had been in the air for almost eight hours,

and according to Curley's calculations we should now be at the last known location of T-3, 88° 17' N., 166° 0' W. But there was no sign of the target.

I opened the door to the navigators' compartment to find out what was going on. I could see that Curley and Mike were frantically checking their calculations; Joe was sitting in the corner with his earphones, apparently trying to get in touch with the leading C-54. The pilots up forward were eagerly peering down at the ice for anything that might resemble the target.

The engineer, who had come on this flight merely because it was his duty, and without any personal desire for the adventure involved, came aft to check the gas.

"What's the score?" I asked him.

"We're lost!" he answered.

From the rear it was difficult to follow what was happening up forward, and I did not wish to disturb the crew by asking questions. I gathered that we had commenced to fly a search pattern, circling the presumed location of the target in legs which formed the sides of a square which gradually extended over a larger area. I watched the gas in the fuselage tank dwindle until there was no more than a few teaspoonfuls of fuel left, when the engineer hastened to switch to the starboard wing tank. There was still an oil leak on the starboard engine.

As the minutes passed the pilots began to look concerned for the first time during the flight. I noticed that they were moving about in their seats, scanning the ice in all directions, and frequently asking questions about radio contact and fuel consumptions. The rest of us said nothing, and the atmosphere became tense.

I pictured the worst: hours of fruitless search until the gas consumption reached the point of no return, and then a race for home. With an oil leak in the right engine, and the weather getting worse, the chances of ending the day on a floe of drift ice in the middle of nowhere could by no means be discounted. And at the best I hated the thought of returning after a sixteen to eighteen hours' flight with nothing achieved.

Following a period of poor radio contact, communication with the three C-54's was now functioning satisfactorily. We received word that the first C-54 with Captain Smith at the controls had been over the target area for more than thirty minutes and was searching for the ice island. They reported a twenty-mile visibility where they were, which was encouraging news.

Then suddenly things began to happen. I was standing by the door to the navigators' cabin when I noticed, judging by the expression on Joe's face and a crack in the radio, that he had received an important message through the earphones. It was Captain Blauchfield, navigator on the leading C-54, who said in his monotonous voice and in his laconic manner: "I may report that T-3 has been located. The island is underneath us just now—and by the way, there is nobody there."

The report was addressed to Major Bradburn, commanding officer of flight D, 10th Air Rescue, in command of the operations as pilot on board the second C-54. Brad asked for a homing signal, and the two remaining C-54's and our C-47 made a heading accordingly.

The atmosphere had varied between grave concern and bright optimism at various stages of the project. At this point the feeling was jubilant, to say the least. George Silk came tearing through the door from the cabin, cheering and waving his arms above his head. Joe was beaming behind the radio in the corner, and Erhart looked pleased with himself. The General had a glow on his face as he told Joe to come forward. It appeared that he had some important instructions to give him.

As for myself, I now felt so certain that the mission would be a success that I began to prepare for the landing. I sorted out our personal bags, pulled out my snowshoes, checked the cameras, and put on my wind-proof trousers and jacket over my regular arctic flying clothing to have all in readiness.

However, it soon became clear that our troubles were far from over. We had been flying by the radio homer for more than thirty minutes when it was discovered that the signals were becoming weaker and weaker: we were flying in the wrong direction, away from the target, toward Siberia. Erhart made a bank and changed our heading 180°. On this course we continued to fly for approximately another thirty minutes, but nothing happened. The engines roared and consumed the precious fuel, and the ship rose and sank on her wings, plowing her way through the frosty sky.

Again the pilots looked concerned, which made the rest of us feel worried. They began to bank while everyone kept a keen watch for signs of the other planes. The two other C-54's were now approaching the target, and reported that they were beginning to orbit over T-3 at different altitudes: one thousand, two thousand and three thousand feet.

The minutes passed. At this stage the navigator was helpless. He had played his part, and when the pilots started to fly on the radio signal, he no longer had any control over the course of events. In a final attempt he made repeated sun shots simultaneously with the navigator on board the leading C-54 to determine whether or not we were approaching each other. When this failed to solve the problem, we were told to watch for flares or rocket signals from the C-54's.

While this was going on a huge mass of floating ice suddenly appeared underneath us—T-3! I looked up and in the distance I could see the three C-54's orbiting overhead, leaving broad vapor trails in the sky as they circled.

We went down and made several low passes over the island to look closely at the surface from low altitude. It soon became obvious that the surface was not so smooth as it had appeared to us during the reconnoitering flight on March 17. Furthermore, a strong wind was blowing across the island, whipping up the snow along the ridges. From this altitude we could distinctly see the wavy surface with a crust of wind-blown snow which looked rough and ragged.

The ship was bouncing along close to the ground when the engines suddenly started to cough. Apparently the gas tank was empty, and the engineer wasted no time in switching to the port wing tank.

Time and time again the pilots made low passes, skimming close over the island, anxiously searching for a suitable place to touch down. But this was no easy task, for the aircraft was bouncing in the gusty wind, and wherever they tried the picture was always the same: a wavy surface with drifts of wind-blown snow. And to top it all, the wind seemed to blow straight across the ridges.

Now there was only one question in our minds: could we get down without crashing on the island? This task was entirely up to the pilots. The rest of us could do nothing, but we watched every move they made through the cabin door, which we had opened in order to hear their instructions.

"Smoke bombs!" shouted the General.

Curley brought out a case of smoke bombs from under the seat; Joe grabbed one and as Erhart made a dive he pulled the safety catch and threw it out through the fuselage door in order to determine the exact direction and the approximate strength of the wind. Joe had quite a job holding the door open with his feet while trying to get rid of the smoke bomb. Sergeant Clohesey was so worried that Joe would fall out that he grabbed him by the neck. Mike and I were on our knees peering out of the window trying to watch the smoke as Erhart pulled up and came back for another pass. The smoke spread out in a stream close to the surface and quickly vanished among the blowing snow! The wind was terrific. Joe threw more bombs, but the result was the same.

"It doesn't look too good," shouted Mike in my ear. I realized how right he was.

Erhart made a new approach, pulled back on the throttles and let down until the rear end of the skis barely touched the ground and dragged across the surface of the snow. We saw the deep ruts made by the skis and realized with a shock that the snow was much deeper than we had anticipated. At first we had a faint hope that it might be less deep elsewhere on the island, and tried several other areas in turn, but the result was always the same. The snow was so deep and the surface so rough that we were in serious doubt about being able to make a successful landing.

Above us circled the three four-engine planes, quietly watching the touch-and-run procedure. These were exciting moments, for this was the climax of anxiety. If this attempt were to prove a failure, it would mean the end of the expedition; months of strenuous preparations would have been in vain, and our hopes of solving some of the intriguing and fascinating mysteries of the Polar Basin would be shattered.

It was a strange experience, and only once before do I recall having had a similar sensation: in the early years of the war when

I found myself sitting in a balloon eight hundred feet above a field in southern England, about to make my first parachute descent. The only difference was that while I had been ordered to leap to the ground through eight hundred feet of space, I had embarked on this adventure of my own free will.

Finally the pilots appeared to have selected a place close to the end of the island to make the landing.

"We are going in. Hold on to your teeth!" shouted Lew Erhart from his seat.

Twice they made a touch-down, dragging the skis several hundred feet, and on the third pass they made a landing, but pulled up again after a run of a few hundred feet, the skis slapping against lumps of ice, and the aircraft skipping from crest to crest. On the fourth attempt a complete landing was made, and the aircraft was quickly slowed down in the deep snow.

We were forced to land across the ridges on account of the wind, but in spite of this the landing was smoother than I had expected.

Under full power we taxied up and down across the ridges, but everywhere the hard-crusted snow was several feet in depth. We bounced along the ice, while the prop blast whipped the snow along the ship as if it were a blizzard, almost obscuring our vision.

At length the aircraft was parked in two feet of snow, close to a ridge about half a mile from the edge of the island, and the engines were cut. Immediately the skis froze to the ground. This was at 1:00 P.M. local time, ten hours after our take-off at Thule.

It was clear sunshine, but as we slowly opened the door, a biting wind hit us in the face. George Silk was the first to get out. He made a dive from the door with his cameras and landed up to his knees in the snow. The General followed, and after him

the rest of us climbed out to have a look. It was extremely cold—
we judged the temperature to be below —60° F.—and the wind
according to our estimate varied between ten and thirty miles
an hour, sweeping the snow across the undulating surface of the
island with the appearance of a restless ocean. Close above the
horizon where the pack ice rose and sank in the arctic mirage,
the yellow sun shone through the frosty mist. In the pale glowing
sky above it the three four-engine aircraft were patiently circling

Here we were at our final destination, on a floating island of
ice at the very northernmost extremity of the earth, only some
hundred miles from the Pole itself.

This was it, T-3, which was to create a unique phase of the
history of modern polar exploration. This was the beginning of
the big adventure for which all our previous training and experience had prepared us, made possible by the knowledge of the
Arctic so painfully gained over the years by those who went before us, the pioneers of the North Polar Basin.

CHAPTER THIRTEEN

Digging In

All eight of us stamped through the snow toward the top of the nearest ridge to orient ourselves on the ice island. From the air T-3 had looked fairly flat but we could now distinctly recognize the wavy appearance of the surface, very similar to the description originally given by Admiral Peary of the shelf ice off Ellesmere Island. From our position on the west side of the island it looked as if the ridges were some hundred or two hundred yards apart and some ten feet high on an average. Judging by the position of the sun, the island was lying with its long axis roughly northeast and southwest.

We had anticipated low temperatures and strong wind, but the deep snow was a great surprise to us all. A preliminary examination revealed that the depth of the snow was about three feet on an average; in a few places it was only six to twelve inches, and the maximum depth was about four feet.

We were at a loss to explain how all this snow had accumulated. We thought that it was all one year's fall, but the depth of the snow on the surrounding pack ice was considerably less than on the island.

The perimeter of the island appeared uneven, and the edge close to the place where we landed was probably five to ten feet above the sea. In most places the hard crust was up to one foot

179

thick, excellent for making snow blocks, but it varied in thickness and strength; often we would break through while walking across it, which made travel without snowshoes very strenuous.

The ice appeared to be the typical glacial ice with a number of small cracks in various directions. Its surface was fairly even and the top layer was porous, with a large number of holes up to a couple of inches in diameter. Later examination revealed that the top layer was as much as four inches thick; under this we reached a layer of dirt ice about a foot or so deep, beyond which there appeared to be clear ice.

It was exceedingly cold so that it was necessary almost constantly to protect our faces from frostbite with our hands and mittens as we stood on the ridge facing the bitter wind. Even our hands needed careful watching, for only a few seconds' exposure while taking photographs, etc., was enough to produce slight frostbite with numbness and whitening of the skin. In spite of our heavy clothing and boots, some of the group complained of cold feet, but the surface crust, the deep snow and our bulky clothing made it difficult to keep up our circulation by moving about.

Never before on any of my arctic journeys have I experienced such cold. To keep the tissues alive by thawing the exposed parts at short intervals with our bare hands or with the back of our mittens, or by jumping vigorously about for greater warmth, was a major occupation which required a great deal of our time. I was watching the engineer: icicles were constantly forming from the hair up under his nose; his nose was turning white and had to be thawed with his bare hands, which in turn were getting numb from the cold.

It has been claimed that severe cold numbs the mind, retarding the mental processes, and leading to inertia and lack of initiative.

Personally I doubt that this theory is correct; it seems to me that the physical conditions and the seemingly insurmountable difficulties involved even in fairly simple tasks are in themselves enough to explain the phenomena referred to.

I had never for a moment since we first began to plan the expedition had any doubts about its feasibility. What I saw from the ridge did not change my opinion, though I must admit that I had previously been too optimistic when judging the prospects for a C-54 landing on the island. However, the possibility that C-54 landings could not be made had been accounted for in our plans. I therefore took it as a matter of course that we were to go ahead with the project.

Joe must have been equally determined, for he was standing there with a bundle of marking flags ready to flag in the supplies to be paradropped as soon as the General gave the signal.

But the General, who was vigorously stamping his feet to keep warm, appeared to be not entirely sold on the idea of the ice island as a base for human existence.

"No C-54 can land in this snow," he insisted.

Erhart was trying to scrape away the snow with his feet to see if the ice beneath it was smooth enough to land on with wheels.

"That's out of the question right here," he agreed, "but perhaps it's better further in where we touched down."

The General took another look across the island. Then he trudged back about a mile along the ruts made by the skis of the C-47 to survey landing conditions.

Joe followed the ridge a few hundred yards southward, testing the depth of the snow with his feet as he walked. In the meanwhile the rest of us walked back to the plane to help Lew Erhart dig out the skis on the C-47, which were frozen in the snow.

Suddenly someone discovered that George Silk had disap-

peared. We looked around in all directions, but he was nowhere
to be seen. Then he eventually appeared on a ridge way off
toward the edge of the island where he was wading through the
snow trying to take pictures. Curley waved him back, for he felt
that we should all remain close to the aircraft in case we had to
take off in a hurry.

"What do you think of it?" I asked Lew.

"I think we can make it in the C-47," he replied. "I wouldn't
mind coming back here tomorrow with another load."

A C-54 dived and thundered across our heads. The General
staggered back through the deep snow, a black silhouette against
the yellow sky. He told Joe that he failed to see how any man
could live on "this thing."

"Let's get out of here while we can," he said, and told Lew
to get everybody on board and to taxi back to the hill to attempt
a take-off. But Joe felt that he had come too far to quit so soon;
he argued that it would be wise to give it a try. The two officers
went off by themselves to talk it over.

In the meantime, there was nothing the rest of us could do but
jump about once in a while to keep our toes alive, and talk about
the weather, how much longer the three C-54's could keep on
circling the island, what the chances were of the C-54's finding a
suitable landing place on the sea ice close to the island, and what
might have happened to the Navy fliers who were on their way
to T-3. But our minds and our eyes were on the two men standing
in the distance with their backs to the wind, shielding their faces
with their hands.

True, the island was not hospitable, but it was solid enough to
be secure, and there was enough suitable snow to construct excellent shelters which would stand the severest weather. Furthermore, we were in the middle of the "Ptarmigan" track where the
58th Weather Reconnaissance Squadron was making the regular

"milk runs" to the Pole. Thus we were assured of reliable contact and of any supplies we might seriously need.

These were some of the arguments Joe put forward in his conference with General Old, who of course carried the final responsibility. At length the General gave in and decided to proceed with the initial stage of the project. I had been impressed many times during the planning with how General Old would let Joe, as the project officer, go ahead according to his own ideas, although the General personally might often not entirely agree with the plans. Now the General himself was the first to pitch in to help unload the supplies. Then he planted the Air Force flag in the snow on the crest which later became our camp site. Joe grinned so that the icicles loosened from his nose.

The C-47 remained on the ground for a period of four hours and twenty minutes while the three C-54's were circling overhead. It had been arranged that if C-54 landings were to be made, Major Bradburn would be the first to land, while a para-doctor team stood by in the second C-54 in case of a serious accident. It was obvious, however, that a wheels-down C-54 landing was impossible on T-3 as conditions were at that time.

From the moment it was decided to go ahead with our plans, things started to happen in rapid succession, and it all went like clockwork. The operation was directed by General Old through radio on board the C-47. Orders were given to the C-54 number 5632 to paradrop four drums of gasoline for refueling the C-47 on the high ridge where we had touched down. The remaining equipment, packed in dropping containers, three thousand pounds in all, was to be paradropped at a dropping zone close to our camp site, clearly marked by red flags made from luminous cloth, which Joe and I had been carrying around with us ever since we landed on the island.

While the C-54 was lining up for the dropping we on the

ground completed the unloading of the C-47. The equipment was tossed out into the snow, loaded on the toboggan sled and pulled by the General, who had harnessed himself in front of it, using one hand to pull and the other to cover his nose, while the rest of us pushed. We left it at the site of the camp a short distance from the airplane, close to the high point of the ridge nearby, where it would be out of the way for the blast of the propellers when the engines were started.

As the C-54 made its approach for the first drop we stopped to watch it. We could see the fuel drum being rolled out through the door as the aircraft thundered across the plains. The pink parachute crackled in the cold air as it opened, but during the opening shock the drum broke loose from the harness, plunged toward the ground and smashed against the ice, gas and snow spouting skyward as it hit.

The General ordered Lew to radio an instruction to the pilot on the C-54 to stay clear of our C-47. "We don't want them to hit us," was his comment.

This was the only mishap; the rest of the equipment came down in excellent condition. It included tents, tarpaulins, rations, clothing, stoves, oil and gasoline. The aluminum containers came down in rows in rapid succession, blinking in the yellow glare of the sun and pendulating under the brightly colored parachute canopies. Pass after pass was made and the load landed with meticulous precision, while the four vapor trails sketched fancy figures in the pale cold sky. It was an impressive sight, and for a moment we almost forgot that we had to keep our noses covered as we stood watching the spectacle.

One of the C-54's had barely enough gasoline for the return journey. It came over and made a last pass before setting course back to Thule.

By this time all our equipment from the C-47 had been unloaded and collected by the camp site. The dropping was completed and the containers lay strewn in rows in the snow. We now had fuel and equipment to live comfortably for at least forty days, and if necessary we could stretch it to last approximately three months.

The four of us who were to remain dug down through three feet of snow to the ice and erected the four-to-six-man double-walled mountain tent as our preliminary shelter. While we prepared to stay, the crew wasted no time in getting ready to leave. General Old bade us farewell and wished us good luck, took one of the sledges and walked toward the ridge where the fuel drums had been landed. Lew and his crew climbed on board the plane. The right engine started at once, but the left one remained dead. He tried it again and again, without success. Finally he put his head through the window and asked how many rations and sleeping bags we had on the island. It looked as if they were all there to stay, when suddenly the engine coughed and sputtered. Finally they taxied under full power through the deep snow across the ridges to the fuel drums. The aircraft was turned against the wind and we could see the men as silhouettes against the setting sun upon the hill, as they rolled the fuel drums through the snow.

It was originally planned that the initial party would consist of Joe, Mike, Paul Green, the radio operator, and myself. At the last minute the plans had been changed to let George Silk take Paul's place. When Silk learned that we might have to remain on the island for thirty days or more before being evacuated, he hurriedly emptied the contents of his kit bag, including some candy, cigarettes and a bottle of whisky, said good-by, wished us good luck and made for the C-47, which was preparing for the take-off.

Joe and Mike walked over to help the air crew fuel the plane while I remained to complete the camp. I fastened some of the ropes which supported the tent securely to the ice with metal pegs. The rest of them I anchored with ski sticks placed as "deadmen" in the snow. It was very awkward working with the stiff rope with my mittens on, but under no circumstances dared I remove the mittens. Finally, I cut large snow blocks with a spade and built up a wall around the tent for protection against the wind, and to prevent the gusts from blowing underneath the tent wall. Every time I bent forward to pick up a snow block, the large hood on my parka fell down over my face and covered my eyes so that I could not see where I was going, and time and time again I stumbled on the tent ropes and smashed the snow block as I fell flat on my face. The only advantage of this annoying situation was that I kept myself warm.

It now appeared that the C-47 was ready for the take-off. The "jato" (jet assisted take-off) bottles which were relied upon to get it away safely from the island, and which had been protected by electrically heated blankets during the outward journey, were fastened on the landing gear above the skis. The men climbed aboard and I watched them as they took off. I could see Joe and Mike walking away from the aircraft; the engines were started and the ship began to move across the rough surface of the island, wobbling like a goose down the slope of the ridge as its speed gradually increased. Then all of a sudden a stream of smoke from the jato bottles appeared from the undercarriage above the skis, and the aircraft surged ahead. It gained speed rapidly and started to lift as the additional twelve hundred horsepower of the jato bottles came into effect. It continued to climb steadily as it passed the camp, and when it reached the edge of the island I could see the jato bottles being dropped. It set course for Ellesmere Island, and the crews of the two remaining C-54's, who had watched the procedure while circling overhead, made a last dive over the tent, waved good-by with the wings and followed the C-47. Soon they disappeared to the south, and the three of us who remained were alone by the Pole.

Now there was no turning back. For a second or two my thoughts went home to those who were waiting for news.

I recalled a similar moment, thirteen years earlier, when two trappers and I sat on the barren shore of Northeast Greenland, gazing after the smoke from the ship that was disappearing out to sea, leaving the three of us behind in a remote corner of the world. A long arctic year lay ahead of us before we would see another vessel.

Now, as the three of us stood there alone on the ice island and watched the plane disappear, we were probably as isolated as anyone can be in this world, and yet we did not feel the solitude.

As the humming of the ten aircraft engines died away we stood for a moment in silence listening to the distant thundering of the restless twisting island grinding relentlessly against the sea ice around it. It was so cold that very little was said as we continued with the work without further ceremonies of any kind. Our main concern was whether or not all the aircraft would be able to return home without any accidents. We realized it would be some time before we knew, because our radio equipment was very limited and would not enable us to communicate directly with the mainland.

"I hate to think of all the things that may happen to any one of those fourteen engines that are turning over up there today," said Joe, "but I have a prejudice against aircraft engines anyhow."

The immediate and most urgent job was to set up a firm camp that would enable us to survive through whatever low temperatures or storms might come. At the same time, we had to collect all our vital equipment and to secure it so that it would not be lost in a blizzard. From previous experience I knew how difficult it can be to find equipment and supplies that have been buried by the snow. In Greenland some trappers once lost their entire supply of fuel outside their cabin during a prolonged and severe snowstorm.

When the tent was securely fastened to the ice and the snow piled all around the edges of it, we gathered and hauled the most essential items of equipment in from the dropping zone and stored them under canvas outside the tent. This was exasperating work, for each container weighed about three hundred pounds, the sled broke frequently through the surface crust, and it was awkward to move about in our bulky clothing. In addition we had to proceed with caution, for the possibility of crevasses still existed. On one occasion I was moving along on my snowshoes toward the edge of the island to collect a bundle of tarpaulins which had been dropped outside the main dropping zone, when suddenly the crust collapsed with a thud over a large area all around me. For a moment it felt as if a snow bridge had collapsed across a crevasse, but I soon realized that it was merely the crust between two ridges.

To prepare for the night, we spread a large tarpaulin on the floor of the tent as insulation against the ice and inflated the rubber air mattresses, which were stiff from the cold. All our sleeping bags were brought inside, each man using two complete sets, one underneath as an insulation against the ice, in addition to a number of blankets.

We tried to produce some heat, but discovered that the kerosene failed to light, nor would the gasoline for our lamps burn until we had used several matches. The kerosene poured like thick syrup, and when it was spilled on the metal of the primus stove it solidified like stearine dripping from a candle. The fuel oil had the consistency of slush ice.

Eventually we succeeded in lighting the two kerosene heaters and the primus stoves. At last having gotten ourselves organized among all the gear in the icy shelter, we opened a case of field rations and prepared our first meal. Sitting on ration cases in a circle around the tent pole, warming our hands over the blazing stoves, we chewed some frozen sausages, biscuits and fruit, and drank hot chocolate which we had prepared.

When we put out the stoves and crawled half-dressed into the chilly sleeping bags to get some rest, after a period of twenty-four hours without sleep, it was late in the night, but it was still as light as it had been when we landed. It was so cold that we had to sleep with our arctic helmets on, and pulled our sweaters over our heads to prevent the biting air from seeping into the bags.

CHAPTER FOURTEEN

The Thirteen Days

We woke up in the morning, Thursday, March 20, with rime frost around the openings of our sleeping bags and on our faces. Several times in the course of the night we had been awakened by tremendous roars and sharp cracks from the far distance as the edge of our revolving island collided with the pack ice and as thermal cracks formed in the ice.

But as we crawled out of the tent we discovered with satisfaction that T-3 had remained solid and safe. We estimated its thickness at two hundred feet, judging by the height of the berg above sea level, which usually constitutes one-ninth of the total thickness.

On this day there would theoretically be midnight sun on the North Pole. Where we were, the sun circled around the island slightly above the horizon almost twenty-four hours a day. This was the beginning of our timeless existence on this island of ice.

To the three of us, alone by the Pole, the clock meant nothing, for there was about the same amount of light day and night, and it was practically impossible to keep track of the time. In addition we had so many different "times" to deal with that it became quite confusing. Owing to the very small distance between each meridian at this high latitude, the "local time" was constantly changing as the restless island drifted with wind and currents

east or west. Then there was the Greenwich mean time to keep
track of; and aircraft from Thule would use Thule time which
was five hours behind Greenwich mean time, and the "Ptarmigan"
B-29's would refer to Alaska time, which was in its turn five hours
behind Thule time. It also was difficult to keep track of direction,
for there were no landmarks to go by.

During breakfast we reviewed our position and discussed our
future plans. As we gathered shivering around the tent pole with
our porridge and sausages, it seemed to us that the first thing to
do was to get an idea of the topography of the island.

Our job at this stage of the project was merely to make a reconnaissance of the island to find out if it would be possible to
establish a permanent station there. For this reason, and because
of the strict weight limitations on the first flight, we were not
equipped to make any scientific observations. Every available
pound of the payload had been used for the bare essentials necessary for our survival.

It was obvious at this point that the success of the project
would depend on whether or not it was possible to bring in the
remainder of the equipment. As it was obvious, too, that it would
be impossible to prepare a landing strip for a C-54 wheels-down
landing on the island at this time without heavy equipment, our
next best solution would be to find a suitable landing strip for the
C-54 on the sea ice, from where supplies could be hauled to the
island by sleds or flown in by the ski-equipped C-47. As we expected a "Ptarmigan" mission that day, there was no time to be
lost, for this would be our only chance to relay an early message
to General Old.

We tied the snowshoes to our feet, wrapped scarves around
our faces and "walked" toward the edge of the island to look for
any frozen leads or flat ice floes suitable for landing. We carried

the two walkie-talkie radio sets underneath our parkas to keep the
batteries warm, in case the "Ptarmigan" B-29 aircraft should appear while we were away from camp.

As we approached the edge of the island we made a halt to
thaw our faces, which had been slightly frostbitten; this was the
coldest day we ever experienced on the island. We looked back
and saw our camp a couple of miles away as a tiny black spot in
the middle of the white shadowless snow. From where we stood
we could clearly see that the center of the island was slightly
elevated, sloping down toward the edges. Around us, on three
sides of the island, we saw the interminable chaos of pack ice with
hummocks rising and sinking in the arctic mirage.

While we were standing there on our snowshoes watching the
pack ice breaking in against the island, being crushed and piling
up along its edges, Joe detected a familiar sound. We held our
breath and listened, and could barely make out the faint hum of
engines in the sky. We gazed toward the south, and eventually we
recognized the familiar vapor trail of a B-29, sketching the four
fuzzy white lines upon the dark blue sky.

Mike had already pulled out his radio set from his coat pocket,
keeping the battery inside his parka. As he pulled out the two
metal rods which served as antennae, crackling began in the tiny
yellow box which he kept in his hand close to his ear. The aircraft
was calling T-3. It was a strange sensation, and it occurred to me
that it must have been equally strange for the "Ptarmigan" crew,
who had been flying across these lifeless wastes for years, con-
sidering it to be the end of the world, suddenly to see life on the
ice and to speak to their previous commanding officer at the Pole.

They reported that they had to maintain their altitude of
eighteen thousand feet in order to conserve fuel. As they passed
directly overhead they were able to read our signals but as they

moved away they could no longer hear us. Soon the batteries cooled and the radio froze, so that Mike had to warm it inside his clothing, while the aircraft made another circle. Eventually, by using both radio sets, Joe sent a message to General Old saying that we were searching for a suitable C-54 landing strip on the sea ice and that he would report the results on our next contact. The contact, however, was very unsatisfactory and unclear, and we found out later that our message was misunderstood and was interpreted as saying that we were making a C-54 landing strip on the island, and that it would be ready by Monday!

As the B-29 disappeared toward the Pole we continued toward the edge of the island and climbed up on the highest hummock, from where we had a fair view of the surrounding pack ice. Close to the island there was an open lead, approximately ten yards wide. Beyond this lead the ice was very coarse and rough and only one floe was as much as fifty by a hundred yards in size.

It was clear to us after this that it would be impossible to find a suitable landing place for the C-54 close to the island without the help of an aircraft, and we returned to the camp, cold and disappointed. As this second alternative had to be abandoned it was evident that only one possibility remained open: to bring the essential equipment and personnel in by ski-equipped C-47, the remainder to be parachuted from C-54's.

In order to increase our comfort and safety we erected the second tent, which was to be our cook tent, or cook shack as Joe named it, and installed the "potbelly" oil stove. It was connected with the oil drum outside the tent by a pipeline in which the half-frozen fuel oil solidified and plugged the opening at regular intervals. Then Mike would have to rush out with his blazing primus stove, which he used as a blowtorch, to heat the pipeline.

Mike was an excellent companion and a very handy man in the

camp. I had not known him more than a few days before our
departure from Alaska, but I soon discovered that he always had
a practical way of doing things, and was very methodical in his
work. Now he was energetically stepping around in his Eskimo
fur boots cutting square snow blocks with his short metal snow
saw, which can also be used as a knife. Like an expert bricklayer
he stacked the snow blocks neatly into a solid wall around the
cook tent to increase the insulation. Eventually this windproof
snow wall reached all the way up to the roof, and provided such
effective insulation that we got rid of the rime frost which had
hitherto been forming constantly on the inside of the single-
walled cook tent. Mike carefully recovered all the pieces of wood
from the one and only wooden box we possessed, and with the
aid of the nails which he saved from it he hammered together a
perfect door for our cook tent. He covered it with canvas to make
it windproof, and built a porch of snow blocks around the doorway. From the ration cases he constructed tables and chairs, so
that each of us had a place to sit down. Joe had his place in the
corner behind the stove, Mike was in front of the radio on the
opposite side and I had my seat by the door. On the table next
to the door we kept the primus stove and the cooking utensils;
our compasses, watches, cameras and knives were hanging by
ropes from the roof. We brought in ice or snow in a large wash
basin, which we melted on the stove for water to drink and to
wash in.

When all this was done we had a warm, tidy and comfortable
place to retreat to where we could thaw our frozen fingers, dry
our clothes and enjoy our meals in peace and comfort. However,
it was so small that when we came in with our clothes full of
snow, we had to enter one at a time to have sufficient room to
undress.

While Mike continued these ingenious improvements of our quarters, Joe and I hauled the rest of the equipment on our toboggan sled to the camp. As the wind increased it became more and more difficult to work outdoors, for slight neglect or short periods of exposure resulted in first-degree frostbite, which we all had almost every day, on our noses, faces and hands. We worked practically all night and crawled into our sleeping bags early in the morning for a few hours' sleep.

As I woke up later in the day and stuck my head out of the bag, I could see the dim light penetrating the ice-covered tent wall. It was icy cold in the tent, but it was warm in the three-layer sleeping bag, though rime frost and icicles framed its opening. We lit the primus stoves before we got out of the bedding in order to raise the temperature as much as possible before dressing. And still it required a considerable amount of will power to roll out of the bag, and the partly frozen zippers gave us considerable trouble.

As we crawled through the narrow opening in the tent the hooks got caught in our bulky parkas, so that we had to help each other to get loose. Then we made a dash for the cook tent, and eventually got the fire going. The breakfast consisted of frozen bread fried in bacon fat with cheese and jam all mixed together. This tasty dish was Joe's invention and it had the advantage of being easy to prepare and of giving us protein, fat and carbohydrate in well-balanced proportions! Our housekeeping arrangements presented no problems. As a rule we took turns melting snow, cooking the meals and washing the dishes. Often these duties were automatically attended to by whoever happened to have the time to spare. For dinner we sometimes voted for the menu to be served, or else the cook had the privilege of selecting the dish he preferred. This system worked very well indeed, and our appetites remained excellent, although all of us lost a few pounds of weight during our stay on the island.

The visibility dwindled in the course of the day, with blowing snow and a blinding white mist. Toward evening the temperature was rising steadily. We expected a blizzard and got busy preparing a storage room in a snow cave to save our equipment.

It had always been Joe's special interest to experiment with ice construction. For this purpose he had purchased a chain saw, but unfortunately we had been unable to bring it on account of the weight restrictions. Instead, we now went ahead to construct a system of snow caves which would enable us to endure the severest weather.

First of all we connected the two tents with a passage by removing the snow down to the ice, and by building up a high wall of snow blocks along the side. In this way we had protection against the wind and could move from one tent to another even in the worst of weather. Joe erected a gentlemen's convenience at the end of another snow passage, where he dug a hole in the snow down to the ice, built up walls of snow blocks around the edge of it, and covered it with a roof of tarpaulin. In order to make it roomier he raised the roof by supporting it with a ski stick in the center, but even so this retreat was so small that one had to be practically an acrobat to use it.

Then we concentrated on the storage room. We dug out a hole in the snow, five by five yards in size, built high walls of snow around it, and roofed it over with a large tarpaulin supported in the center by three empty drop drums stacked one on top of the other. This was very strenuous work. It took us several hours to shovel out the hard-packed snow to begin with. While I cut the snow blocks with a long snow knife and carried them through the deep snow to the edge of the snow hole, Joe did the actual building, trimming the blocks to the required size so that they would fit together to make almost airtight walls. The walls were high enough to allow a man to stand upright inside the room. After all our equipment was brought inside we put the tarpaulin in place and securely anchored it into the snow with "deadmen." Then for extra security we froze the edges of the ropes into the ice by pouring water into the ice holes in which they were fastened.

During the first days on the island we devoted all our time to getting our quarters established. On March 22, our fourth day on the island, when it was considerably milder, we prepared new sleeping quarters in a snow cave adjacent to the storage room. This snow cave, or snow house, was built in the same way as the storage room, and was of similar size. The wind had died down, the flag was hanging quietly from the mast, and the visibility was almost nil, so that we could see nothing outside our camp.

At three o'clock in the afternoon the storm broke. Just as we had practically completed the sleeping quarters and were anchoring the tarpaulin, it started to blow. The wind came up suddenly from the northwest and increased to gale force in the course of the evening, with a choking blizzard.

We sat around the stove until midnight, when we made a dive for the sleeping tent. While the blizzard raged outside we lay in our sleeping bags listening to the roaring gale whipping the canvas of the tent, popping it like a shotgun, and the thunder of ice colliding with the moving island. Time after time we expected the tent to take off or the canvas to tear apart in the violent gusts, and we were prepared for the worst. But to our surprise the tent remained intact through the gale. The blizzard penetrated the tiny openings in the fabric around the door and gradually covered the floor and our equipment with fine powdery snow.

We had placed the three large sleeping bags like spokes of a wheel out from the tent pole in the center, our heads toward the wall. Between our bags we had stacked our rucksacks and personal belongings. The stoves were standing on ration cases in a circle around the tent pole, and next to the door were our guns, snowshoes, extra rations, our "Gibson Girl" radio set which was to be used only to send out distress signals in an emergency, and various odd items of equipment, packed in bags for protection against the snow. There was hardly a square foot of empty space. Here, lying half-dressed in our bags, with the rest of our clothing pulled inside or placed on top of them so we could find it in a hurry, we spent the hours, tossing about sleeplessly, while the blizzard continued. From time to time we poked our heads out of the bags to keep an eye on the tent and our equipment, and once in a while one of us would make a remark; but in the roaring and howling gale it was very difficult to hear what was said, so for the most part we remained silent with our thoughts. I had made up my mind that if the tent blew away there was nothing to do but to remain in the bag until the blizzard was over.

It continued to blow for twenty-four hours. Then the wind died down as suddenly as it had come and the sun appeared, and it once more became terribly cold. When we came out of the tent we could hardly recognize the camp, for huge snowdrifts covered it almost completely. That day, March 23, we saw the midnight sun for the first time in the glowing sky to the north.

After a reconnaissance trip to the west edge of the island, where we saw nothing but pack ice in all directions without any open leads, we moved into the new snow cave which was to be our future sleeping quarters. We covered the snow walls with blankets and tarpaulins, and used a double blanket as a door. One kerosene heater supplied sufficient heat to make the cave comfortably warm.

Joe had been very anxious to move into the new cave for he

had no confidence in the double-walled mountain tent. We rolled
out our bags on bunks of snow blocks along the walls, but a few
hours after we had put out the kerosene lamp and the heater, I
heard someone grunt like a bear, and stumble out through the
door. It was Joe, who was unable to sleep in our luxurious quarters. When we went out to the cook shack in the morning we
found him asleep on the ration cases in a corner of the tent by
the stove.

Joe was an amazing fellow. I had known him long before we
started on the expedition, and yet during our stay on the island
he continually surprised me by revealing new abilities, an unusually broad knowledge and wide experience, as well as personal
qualities which I had not noticed before. His modesty and his
habit of always keeping himself in the background made him
hard to find out about all at once. But as my impressions deep-
ened during our long discussions around the potbelly stove in the
cook tent I realized that it would be hard to find a better companion for an arctic expedition.

In the afternoon of March 24 we made a long exploratory trip
to the northwest end of the island, looking for possible landing
places. We marched for hours on our snowshoes against the numbing wind without being able to reach the northern shore of the
island, which in a straight line should be about eight miles away
from camp. A short distance to the north of our camp we found
a large flat area suitable for ski landings although the snow was
very deep.

We took advantage of the fine weather to examine the profile
of the ice by digging vertical holes or shafts with picks and
shovels, and Joe collected samples of the dirt from the upper layer
of the ice. These and later examinations convinced us that the
island consisted of solid glacial ice.

The next morning I was suddenly awakened by a peculiar noise which sounded like the roaring engines of an aircraft. I jumped out of the bag, called Mike and grabbed whatever clothes I could find in the dark cave. As I dashed out through the tunnel into the open I saw a B-29 making low passes over the camp.

As Mike and I rushed into the cook shack we found that Joe had been up early, lit the fire, and was now sitting fast asleep in front of the red-hot stove. In his excitement when he woke up, he grabbed one of the small radio sets and ran outside bare-headed and without mittens. Mike, operating the larger set on the one-hundred-meter band, established contact with the air-craft, and the signals came so loud and clear that I could read them several yards away from the receiver. I put my head out through the tent door and saw Joe standing there in the cold, with his pants dropped down to his knees, eagerly operating the radio set.

Major Soderberg, who was the aircraft commander, kept cir-cling the camp while we talked to each other, exchanging news and information. He conveyed a message from General Old asking if there was anything we needed which could be dropped to us by parachute. He also requested information about the landing strip for a C-54 which they thought we were in the process of mak-ing. We learned that all aircraft had returned safely on March 19 after the mission, and eventually reached Alaska, but that Captain Lew Erhart, whom Major Soderberg had met in the bar the other night, was to return in the ski-equipped C-47 to Thule in the near future. Other than this, there was no definite information about the future plans for the project; but he brought the good news that I was the proud father of a son, born on the 22nd of March in Fairbanks, Alaska.

Joe sent a message to General Old saying that as a result of surface reconnaissance we had found the island to consist of solid glacial ice, and that it was suitable as a base for a permanent camp. We were by no means ready to be evacuated and stated that Jamesway huts were not essential to maintain a permanent camp at this time. (These huts are portable, prefabricated shelters consisting of insulating material stretched over wooden frames.) We had found it would be impossible to prepare a landing strip for a C-54 on the island until after the melting season was over. Joe asked that the radio operator, Captain Green, and the geophysicist, Dr. Crary, with his assistant, Mr. Cotell, be brought in one way or another as soon as possible, together with the communications equipment and the meteorological station. The remaining equipment could be parachuted. They gave us the exact time, position and the present orientation of the island, and continued on their course. This had been an exciting event for us all, and as the sound of the engines died away, we set about celebrating the birth of my son with a bottle of whisky and a birthday cake which my wife had sent along in my rucksack for the occasion. The whisky was frozen solid and was placed on the stove to thaw while we cut the hard-frozen cake in three pieces with a handsaw.

As we passed the cigars around our spirits were high, although at this point we were still in suspense about our future prospects, since we did not know whether the project was to be continued, or whether the C-47 was on its way to evacuate the party.

On Wednesday, March 26, we had completed our first week on the island. It was still very cold, between fifty and sixty below, and clear, with a constant slight breeze from west or east. We saw open water over a large area in the west, where the frost fog appeared.

By now we were well organized in our camp, and life began to be comfortable and easy, and the work a matter of routine. We slept well in our cozy snow cave, our appetites were excellent, and no one had any physical complaints, save backaches caused by lifting and pulling the heavy equipment in the deep snow.

A survey of the ration supplies gathered in the storage cave revealed that with our present rate of consumption we could live comfortably for another month or two on unrestricted rations; but we had only little more than a gallon left of the gasoline for the Coleman lamps, so that strict rationing might become necessary.

In the evening, as we were sitting quietly writing our diaries in the cook tent, we suddenly heard a thud, and felt a tremendous crack in the ice. At the same time we heard the snow crust break and the snow wall outside the tent collapsed on one side. For a moment we thought that it was a bear walking by the tent, so we grabbed the rifle and dashed out, but discovered that the noise we had heard must have been the result of a collision between the pack ice and the island.

The following day, the ninth day of our stay, it was overcast with light snow. It looked as if a storm were approaching; the visibility was poor and we were unable to see the sun. We noticed tremendous movements in the pack ice and heard thunders and crashing roars in the west.

We had intended to reconnoiter the interior of the island, but were prevented by the weather, so we whiled the time away by repairing the collapsed snow wall and enlarging the examination shaft through the ice.

In the course of the night the wind changed to the south; it continued to snow the next day, when the visibility was less than a hundred yards, and the temperature was gradually rising. We anticipated a considerable northward drift with this strong wind from the south, and expected to reach the 89th parallel soon.

We remained sitting around the fire while Joe talked philosophy. He dwelt on the evolution of man's ideas about freedom, the forward course of scientific discovery and the technical foundation for flights through space, and interplanetary communication. He developed his theories for changing the climate of the Polar Basin by breaking the steady overcast during the summer by artificial means, thus increasing the solar heat absorbed by the Arctic Ocean, and we speculated on the possible consequences of this for the nations bordering the polar regions. We pulled out our maps and spent some enjoyable hours visualizing the future developments of the project which we were now engaged in, and we developed ideas for future expeditions into the few areas of the arctic regions still unaffected by civilization. Eventually Mike brought us back to earth by telling us about his hunting in Alaska, and the time he chased polar bears in the drift ice thirty miles north of Barter Island. Finally at 4:00 A.M. we retired.

It was pitch black in the snow cave when I was awakened to partial consciousness by something moving about on the ice floor. It seemed to be coming toward me slowly, snorting and sniffing, and then I had a sensation of warm air being breathed down my neck. Instantaneously I was wide awake for I thought for certain it was a bear that had sneaked through the tunnel. I leaped out of the bag—and knocked my head against Mike who was crawling about on the floor in search of his mukluks!

The wind increased in the course of the day and soon the tent wall was caving under its pressure. The snow was blowing through the small openings around the door and eventually covered the floor with large drifts. By five o'clock in the evening there was a regular blizzard and we were forced to seal the entrance to our storage cave. Any outdoor activities were out of the question, so we spent the time in the tent preparing our notes from the observations we had made during the reconnaissance.

After midnight we retired into the snow cave, lit the two sports heaters, and covered the entrance. We sat there on our sleeping bags, again discussing the prospects of the project. At this stage they did not seem too bright, for we had so far had no definite information indicating that the Alaskan Air Command had agreed to go ahead. We were waiting for the cave to get warm enough for us to crawl into our bags in comfort, when we were startled by the roar of engines overhead. We sprang to our feet and looked at each other; we could hardly believe it, for the weather was foul and the visibility almost nil.

We ran out through the tunnels into the cook tent to the radio. At this time we could not see the aircraft but as we tuned in on the one-hundred-meter band we heard Ptarmigan 2195, aircraft Commander Captain McGibney, calling T-3, asking for Colonel Fletcher. A very lively radio communication followed.

The B-29 orbited over the camp for almost half an hour while they reported that a C-54 and a C-47 with Captain Smith and Captain Erhart of the 10th Rescue had left Alaska and had just landed at Thule. They had brought with them 7,400 feet of rope and 75 parachutes for para-dropping equipment on T-3. They had also brought George Silk, the *Life* photographer, who was to join the T-3 party once more, and Colonel Gill, commanding officer of the 2107th Air Weather Group, who would remain at Thule for two weeks to supervise operations. The two aircraft were scheduled to arrive at T-3 Sunday, March 30, at 9:00 A.M. local time, weather permitting. The pilots requested that we stand by to home them in on our radio if necessary. Additional personnel would come out on the first C-47 flight. In other words: the project was to be continued, and I would return to Thule on the first C-47 in order to assist in the organization of equipment to be sent in to T-3.

We asked them if they had seen anything of the Navy, since we had expected them here long ago. They told us that the Navy fliers, after one unsuccessful attempt when they returned with engine failure, had started from Point Barrow two days ago, and had landed for refueling on the pack ice at 76° N. During take-off they had damaged the landing gear, and the crew of nine were stranded on the ice.

Captain McGibney gave a time signal, and reported our position as being 88° 08′ N., 152° W. This astounded us. If they were right we had been drifting far to the east, while with the strong southerly wind that we had had the last few days, we expected to be close to the 89th parallel. We had no way of checking it, however, for our sextant had been left in the C-47 by mistake the day we landed.

As we stepped outside the tent after they had signed off, there was a lull in the storm, and as the clouds broke we caught a glimpse of the superfortress as it disappeared southward.

This was probably our happiest moment during the entire expedition. Now we knew that the road was clear ahead. The uncertainty and doubt that had prevailed the past few days gave way to a spirit of overwhelming optimism. The strenuous months of preparations would now at last be paying off in full. So far our part of the project had been an exciting adventure. Now it would mean the beginning of an important undertaking of lasting scientific value, which in the months, and perhaps years, to come would find the answers to some of the unsolved mysteries of the Arctic.

For a few hours the atmosphere in the cook tent was jubilant.

Then we settled down to tackle the practical problems immediately ahead.

Our next step would be to mark a suitable landing strip for the C-47 and a dropping zone for the C-54, but we were hindered by the weather. The blizzard continued all through Saturday, March 29. Throughout the night we waited for the storm to cease. Early the following morning the wind died down sufficiently to enable us to go out to mark the runway. In the white-out conditions, with blowing snow along the ground, and without shadows or contrasts, the surface relief was deceiving. From a distance the selected area looked smooth and flat, but as we walked along the strip, placing markers at every hundred yards, we soon discovered the unevenness and many concealed conical ice formations which could damage the skis. We also found that the snow varied greatly in depth. We went back and forth, up and down for hours, and one possibility after the other had to be abandoned. Since the wind was blowing from the south, the direction of the strip had to run north-south, i.e., along the ridges. In this respect conditions now were more favorable than during our first landing, when we had to land across the ridges.

It was quite awkward walking with snowshoes across the very uneven hard-packed snow crust. Often, as we were moving along without watching where we were going, we would stumble and fall. While I always used the long trail type of snowshoes, Joe insisted he had more maneuverability using the short type, commonly known as "bear paws." These, in contrast to the trail type, are not turned up in front, so that they catch more in the concealed ice mounds and other obstacles. Time and time again when I turned around I would see Joe lying on his back with his snowshoes in the air, fighting to get back onto his feet. In the long run this can be rather annoying and I admired Joe for his self-control; I could see that he was mad, but he never said a word.

After eight attempts we succeeded in finding a suitable strip which we marked by flags. It was a ridge where for 500 feet in the center portion the snow was only six inches deep. The entire length of the runway was 2,100 feet.

We marked a dropping zone close to the camp with a row of flags and returned to the cook tent where Mike had been standing by on the radio in case the two aircraft arrived. In the afternoon the wind came up from the south and the visibility was very poor with blowing snow so that we no longer could see the flags along the runway.

At about nine o'clock in the morning of March 31, a C-54 suddenly appeared in the sky above the camp, and half an hour later the C-47 circled the island. The C-54 immediately proceeded to drop the equipment, which in spite of the strong wind was landed without damage of any kind. First came the heavy fuel drums, followed by aluminum containers with all kinds of equipment and supplies, and finally they made several low passes, tossing out ration cases without parachutes, which landed in the snow in good condition.

After one low pass over the runway, where Joe and I were standing with the portable radio set watching the procedure, the C-47 landed and as it touched the ground disappeared in a cloud of snow whipped up by the propellers. For a moment we thought it had crashed or turned over. Unfortunately Lew Erhart had failed to see our small markers on account of the white-out and he landed to the left of the marked runway. The landing was very rough and he damaged the left ski. With the engines roaring he taxied up the runway like a snowplow.

When the door opened after the engines died down, Joe's dog, Tundra, rolled out, followed by Captain Green and Dr. Crary. They brought with them radio equipment and a power plant as well as a small meteorological station.

Lew Erhart brought out a large sign nailed to a long pole which he planted in the snow. We gathered around it and cheered as we read "Fletcher's Ice Island" painted in white letters against a blue background. General Old had decided to name the ice island for the man who had more or less gambled his entire career on the project. No name could have been more appropriate.

The aircraft was unloaded in a hurry. We collected as many of the parachutes as possible and brought them on board while the engines were started at short intervals to keep them warm. The C-54 continued to orbit overhead. Then two drums of gasoline were dropped from the C-54 and hauled on the sled to the C-47, which was refueled.

At about 1:00 P.M. we were ready to take off. The skis were dug out of the snow, I said good-by to my companions, and under full power Lew turned the ship about and we began to move along the runway. We humped along over the ice as we gained speed, and suddenly the rattle and shaking ceased as we were airborne. We banked, and as we passed the camp on our way home I saw the four men and a dog standing by the camp site surrounded by the scattered equipment. When we had landed thirteen days earlier the snow was unbroken, but now there were tracks and footprints in all directions.

On this return flight the crew consisted of Lew Erhart, pilot, Major L. Brown, co-pilot, Captain E. Curley, navigator, and Sergeant H. Clohesey, engineer, while I was the only passenger. Of this crew, Erhart, Curley and Clohesey, who had taken part in the initial landing March 19, were awarded the air medal for their achievements.

The left landing gear had apparently been severely damaged during landing and take-off, for it could no longer be retracted, so we proceeded toward Thule with the left ski hanging down, making only 120 miles an hour.

We continued to fly hour after hour, making slow progress toward the land. As we approached Alert on the north coast of Ellesmere Island we ran into fog, and it was questionable whether we would have gas enough to reach Thule. The C-54, however, which was circling over the Robertson Channel between Greenland and Ellesmere Island waiting for us, reported a thirty-five-mile-an-hour tail wind, so it was decided to take a chance. The weather was clear south of Alert, so if we ran out of gas we could count on being able to land on the drift ice to refuel by gasoline parachuted from the C-54.

We continued the flight across the northwest corner of Greenland in clear moonlight, and flew in over Thule at midnight.

There had been some doubt whether the left landing gear would function and hold up during landing. To prepare for trouble the load was shifted forward, and the door was opened before we made the final approach. Lew lowered the ship gently to the ground until the main gear barely touched the runway. The left wheel, which was out of line, pulled us to the left, and for a moment it felt as if we were going to get off the runway. But Lew remained in control of the plane, and brought her to a complete stop in front of the flight line at Thule.

CHAPTER FIFTEEN

The Scientific Station on a Floating Island of Ice

At Thule, Colonel Gill, commanding officer of the 2107th Air Weather Group, was now monitoring the operations, since the T-3 base would be under the jurisdiction of the weather group, and the assistant project officer, Lieutenant Danner, was faithfully taking care of the supply problem as usual. On the basis of my knowledge of conditions on the ice island, I was able to help him in the arrangement of supplies and priorities. This work was greatly facilitated after the first radio contact was established between T-3 and Thule on April 2, the day after I returned from the island.

We had figured out that two additional C-47 missions, as well as the two or three C-54 drop missions, were needed to complete the project and to bring in the necessary number of personnel and equipment to maintain the permanent station for a period of three months. We thought it could be accomplished within the next few days.

We had carefully gone through the equipment, and decided that only the bulky Jamesway huts, the large Diesel power plant, the towers for the wind chargers, and some very delicate instruments had to be flown in by the C-47. The rest of it, including rations, most of the radio equipment and instruments for the weather station, as well as the generators for the wind chargers, could be dropped by parachute. Other supplies, such as lumber cut in suitable lengths, beds and the cases of field rations could be thrown out from the C-54 without parachutes. This was eventually done very successfully, and saved us much trouble; for all parachutes used for the paradrops had to be collected and returned by the C-47 and repacked before they could be used again.

A complication occurred, however, when on April 1 Lieutenant Colonel William P. Benedict and a civilian, Mr. Fritz W. Awe, formerly a bush pilot in Alaska, arrived at Thule with two weasels which they insisted on bringing to T-3 for the purpose of making a C-54 runway, in accordance with instructions from the Alaskan Air Command—a proposition which I assured them emphatically would be impossible. In addition, the C-47 could make only two more missions to T-3 before it was due for a major inspection. I therefore argued that it would be wiser to utilize the remaining flying time of the C-47 to take in the supplies that would wind up the first phase of the project. Then, at a later stage, if it were still desirable, the weasels could be flown in, for although it was highly improbable that a weasel would be capable of packing the snow sufficiently to make a snow runway for a C-54, it would be useful as transportation for the T-3 party on their research expeditions to various parts of the island.

In the face of this argument they went ahead and did it anyway. Major Bradburn apparently felt that if there was even a small chance of building a C-54 runway with the aid of the weasels, it was worth a try, for if the C-54's could land on T-3, no further C-47 missions would be necessary.

On Thursday, April 3, the C-47 left at seven o'clock in the morning with one weasel and Colonel Benedict and Mr. Awe on board, as well as Mr. Silk. Two hours later the C-54 departed with a load of four thousand pounds. The mission was very successful; after a ten-hour flight against a strong head wind the C-47 made a perfect landing with the heavy load, and the equipment, including the weasel, was unloaded within an hour. But when Joe Fletcher saw the weasel being rolled out of the aircraft onto a platform made of empty gasoline drums, he shook his head.

Another six thousand pounds of supplies, among other things a generator, part of a Jamesway hut, some lumber and various tools were loaded on the C-54 on April 4. It took off in the morning and reached T-3 without incident, but during the dropping one of the parts of the Jamesway hut almost hit the tail of the aircraft. On this flight unfavorable weather with low stratus was encountered for the first time. This overcast had been our greatest concern from the start, and every effort was now made to speed up the operation and complete the project before the onset of the lasting polar mist.

On the afternoon of April 5 we finished the loading of 3,800 pounds on the C-47, including the Diesel power plant, one Jamesway hut, a wind charger and the remainder of the scientific equipment for the geophysicist. When this mission was completed only one more paradrop by the C-54 would be needed to bring in everything necessary for the temporary operation of the permanent camp. The huge warehouse where we had stored our equipment at Thule was now almost empty.

The plan was for the C-47 to take off at 1:00 P.M. the next day, April 6, and after landing the equipment to return to Thule. The C-54, No. 5632, would take off two or three hours later to fly top cover for the C-47 to the ice island, from where it would return directly to Alaska for a major inspection, the second C-54 remaining at Thule for the final drop mission later. As I had now fulfilled my particular part of the project, I was to return to my duties in Alaska with the C-54.

However, the weather report for April 6 was unfavorable. A low-pressure center was moving from the east and we expected strong winds and snow with low visibility. It was therefore decided to wait for a further weather report on April 6.

In the middle of the night Lieutenant Danner woke me up with a radio message announcing that the two Navy aircraft from "Skijump II" were on their way to Thule via T-3. These two aircraft were ski-equipped Neptune bombers which had been engaged in the Navy's "Skijump" operations in the pack ice north of Alaska, the purpose of which was to carry out oceanographic studies in the Arctic Ocean. This operation was a continuation of a similar project, "Skijump I," the previous year.

April 6 came with poor visibility, blowing snow and strong winds with tremendous gusts from the edge of the inland ice. In spite of this it was decided to carry on as planned. I hurried to pack my belongings and was eager to go, for this would be my first trip back to T-3. Even though I would only be flying over it, I was very anxious to see how they were getting along.

Just before we were ready to take off, an alarming radio message reported that the two Navy P2-V's had landed on T-3 but that one of them was stuck with engine failure and needed an engine change. At the same time, Joe Fletcher wired to say that the C-47 should stand by until further notice. On the basis of these messages it was decided to wait until the second P2-V had arrived at Thule from T-3, when further details would be available.

It landed at three o'clock in the afternoon. The pilot explained that both aircraft had made a ski landing on T-3, heavily loaded

HAMS

with a large number of passengers. Following a few hours' visit at the camp, they once more took to the air, but in Commander Coley's aircraft they had forgotten to remove the pins in the landing gear prior to take-off so that it could not be retracted. Consequently he had to come back for another landing. During the second take-off one of his engines failed, and he had to return to the island, where he was stuck with a total of thirteen men, including George Silk, who was thus unable to get back with his story. *TOO BAD! SENT OUT ON 20 METERS*

Major Bradburn decided we would go ahead as planned. At five o'clock in the afternoon, I watched the C-47 take to the air with Lieutenant Danner and Mr. Cotell on board, and disappear toward the stormy sky. We gathered our belongings, said farewell to our friends and took off in the C-54 at 7:30 in the evening in a thirty-five-mile-an-hour wind with blowing snow. We homed in on the radio beam on T-3 and arrived over the island at 87° 58' N., 156° 0' W. an hour past midnight. At that time the C-47 had already landed.

The weather was perfect. The ice island had been visible more than fifty miles out, looking like a white aircraft carrier in the middle of the pack ice.

As we circled the island we saw the base underneath us, 10,-000 feet below, humming with activity, with a permanent station surrounded by 75,000 pounds of equipment. What a change since our first landing only three weeks earlier. Great numbers of men were running in all directions around the camp where only the three of us had struggled along on snowshoes; two aircraft were parked near the runway which we had marked out in trackless, wind-blown snow; a weasel was pulling equipment between the dropping zone and the permanent building, while not long ago we toiled through the snow crust with a sled. Where there once was nothing but snow caves covered with tarpaulins and tents below the flying flag, there was now the VIP-quarters supplied with electricity and heat, in which the Navy guests were comfortably billeted. It was with a feeling of satisfaction that I realized that our dream of a semi-permanent scientific station in the middle of the inaccessible Polar Sea had become a reality.

HAMS (ARCTIC HEROES)

The accident to the Navy plane had occurred at a most inopportune moment, when thousands of pounds of vital equipment were scattered in the snow, and when the T-3 party urgently needed to use all its time and effort to consolidate the station and to establish routine operations. Now, however, all this was being held up. To fly a bulky thirty-five-hundred-pound engine for the Navy bomber in to T-3 was a major operation, for it was too big and heavy to be taken in by a C-47. It now became imperative, therefore, to build a runway to enable a C-54 to land with the engine and the necessary material for an engine change out on the ice.

OH THE INCONSIDERATE NAVY!

Colonel Benedict's weasel project had been making slow progress, but eventually the snow was packed down along the entire strip, and on April 18 the optimistic Benedict flagged in the C-54, loaded with some 13,500 pounds, including a complete engine, and "A" frame, a prefabricated working shelter and gasoline aircraft heaters. The four-engine aircraft of the 54th Troop Carrier Squadron circled the island, made the final approach and lowered its wheels on the packed snow crust. For a moment the wheels rolled on the snow under the roaring monster, while the fifteen islanders held their breaths. Then the nose wheel broke through the crust and skidded along the surface of the ice.

The Neptune engine was delivered intact, but in the process another aircraft was thus marooned on the island, where the population was now suddenly increased to thirty-three. The crew tried in vain to shovel the snow away in front of the wheels for a take-off, but finally, after several unsuccessful attempts, they were forced to give up in the face of a hopeless situation.

A small snow grader had to be flown in by the old workhorse, the C-47, and in a few days a little more than a thousand feet of runway was cleared so that the C-54 could get out.

After the complete engine change the Navy patrol bomber got away with all the extra personnel and landed at Thule on April 24. In the meanwhile the meteorological station had been put into operation, and regular weather reports reached the mainland at six-hour intervals, supplying valuable data for long-range weather predictions. The first report had been sent on April 2, addressed to General Senter, commanding officer of the U. S. Air Weather Service, and read: "Temperature 17 degrees below zero, wind calm, and visibility 20 miles."

Now that all the visitors had gone, and the permanent station had been established, the ice islanders could really settle down to their work. This formed the beginning of the third and final stage of Project Icicle: the full-scale scientific exploitation of the ice island as a steppingstone for the exploration of the North Polar Basin.

Since April 1, 1952, the geophysicist, Dr. A. P. Crary, assisted by R. D. Cotell, has been engaged in an active research program on T-3, directed in general toward the study of the physical characteristics of the ice island, the movement of the ice and the depth of the Polar Sea. At times they have had to work days and nights on end without any sleep at all, for in addition to their scientific duties they have had to pitch in with the rest of the ice islanders hauling equipment and building the station.

As the station was finally organized and the daily observations and scientific duties became a matter of routine, the ice islanders took advantage of the favorable spring weather to extend the scientific observations to other areas of the Polar Basin, staging from the island.

On May 3, a ski-and-wheel-equipped C-47 with Lieutenant Colonel Benedict as pilot and Joe Fletcher as co-pilot landed on an old thick floe on the geographical North Pole, spending three hours and ten minutes on the ice to enable Dr. Crary and Mr. Cotell to measure the depth of the ocean (14,150 feet) and the pull of the gravity of the earth at this point. They returned to T-3 only 135 miles away in less than an hour's flying time, homing in on the radio beacon.

Here they refueled and flew on toward Ellesmere Island and landed on T-1. From there they continued and landed on the shelf ice off Ellesmere to ascertain the origin of the ice islands. They found the features of the shelf ice identical to those of the ice islands; there can no longer be any doubt that this is where they originate. Perhaps the practical consequence of this will be that in the future ice islanders may establish themselves on suitable portions of the shelf ice, which then by artificial means can be broken loose from the glacial fringe and set adrift in the Polar Sea as floating scientific stations!

As the group from T-3 were flying along the edge of the shelf ice, Joe discovered an object sticking up from the snow on the land. Benedict banked and put the aircraft down on the ground. They found it was a cache left by Godfrey Hansen for Roald Amundsen in 1920, and a sign post erected by Peary when he set out on his 413-mile journey to the North Pole in 1909. Three broken sled runners, tied to form a tripod, marked the cache of wood-crated metal boxes—still there after thirty-two years of exposure to arctic gales and storms.

On May 15 we succeeded for the first time, through the ama-

ARCTIC HEROE BADGE #1

teur radio operator Lieutenant Milan, in establishing direct contact from Alaska with the ice island party, which now consisted of Joe Fletcher, Paul Green, Bert Crary and Bob Cotell. From then on we were able to talk to the group almost daily and could follow them day by day as their scientific exploration progressed.

On the basis of their regular sextant observations, measuring the vertical angles of the sun and the moon, they were able to calculate the exact location of Fletcher's Ice Island at a few days' intervals. These observations have shown that the island is moving in zigzags, generally speaking in conformity with the wind force, confirming the findings of Nansen and H. U. Sverdrup on the movement of the drift ice.

Since we landed on the island on March 19, 1952, its general movement has been in an easterly direction, the most northerly point reached being 88° 50′ N. on May 16, 1952. The rate and direction of the movement are directly related to the speed and the direction of the wind, which the geophysicists have concluded is, therefore, the predominant factor. They have also confirmed our earlier findings, made from the air, that the island travels from one to two miles a day.

They found no positive evidence of a permanent current in this part of the North Polar Basin. In order to examine this point further, they have determined the relative motions of ice and water down to depths of twelve hundred feet by a drag-type current meter suspended through a hole in the sea ice. These observations bear out the theory that the movement of the ice island is mainly due to the wind, and that permanent sea currents, if any, are insignificant. ERRONEOUS SEE H.O. PUBS.

Every week the true bearing of the island has been determined. During the spring the island remained pretty much in the same heading, but during the summer, rotations of up to eighty degrees in a clockwise manner were recorded. This confirms our early observations during the initial phase of the project, when the island twisted and turned so that we had difficulty in keeping track of our bearings.

In addition to these movements a slight tilting of the island during strong winds has been observed, with the aid of a very sensitive bubble level, placed on one of the ridges near the camp.

A detailed topographical survey of the ice island has led to the conclusion that the peculiar ice bumps, a couple of feet high and five to ten feet in diameter, which we noticed on top of the ridges, and one of which damaged the ski on the C-47, are pressure bubbles, probably created by pressure from trapped "underground" water. *possible artesian wells?*

During an excursion in the weasel on a sunny day in May, Bert Crary and Joe discovered large deposits of rocks on the eastern side of the island, about eight miles from camp. Some of them were over a ton in weight, and must have been deposited on the island when it was landfast or near the shore. Closer examination revealed that this end of the island was almost completely covered with rock and gravel.

In order to study the vertical structure of the ice at different depths, core holes were made with a specially constructed drill, a four-inch ice corer, with which they were able to bore down more than fifty feet into the ice. The drill is so constructed that the ice core can be lifted out of the hole and examined.

They found that underneath the heavy top dirt layer which we had seen when we landed on T-3, there were smaller layers of dirt, in general one foot apart; in the fifty-two-foot core they counted together fifty-eight different layers. When the age of these dirt layers has been determined by the carbon 14 analysis, significant knowledge may be gained of the history of the ice island.

Once when they were drilling a test hole in the vicinity of the camp, the corer suddenly plunged into a fresh-water lake below eight feet of ice, the water layer itself being eight feet deep. The water was under such pressure that it spouted out of the test hole like a geyser as the drill broke through the ice. This "underground" lake, which had been formed by melt water accumulated in a trough between two ridges during the melting in the fall, was from then on used as a well for drinking water.

By preliminary seismic profiling of the island, Crary determined the thickness of T-3 to be approximately 200 feet. From his later measurements, however, it appears that this figure is too high, and that the average thickness is probably no more than 160 feet.

The depth of the ocean along the drift of the ice island was determined at intervals of a few days by exploding charges of dynamite and recording the return echoes by seismographs. These measurements have not only given the actual depth of the ocean but also the thickness of the sediment layer on the bottom.

Generally speaking the depth varied between 12,300 and 12,800 feet, except for certain areas along the eastern part of the drift where they made the interesting discovery of two sea mounts which rise to heights over 5,000 feet above the bottom of the sea. When T-3 drifted over these mountains, a giant canyon with sheer precipices over 4,000 feet high was discovered. These seismic studies also reveal that the entire Polar Sea is not a uniformly deep basin as previously believed, but that the part of it across which T-3 drifted is quite irregular and varies greatly in depth. The depths were greater in the west, while further east depths of no more than 5,000 feet were observed.

Measurements of the ocean temperature have in general confirmed Nansen's original findings, with evidence of warm Atlantic water at 1,000 to 1,500 feet below the surface. In addition, they discovered a persistent layer of warm water at 400 feet, the origin of which is still obscure. The cables needed for these measurements were lowered and raised with the aid of a chain saw motor adapted for this purpose.

These oceanographical studies were eventually taken over by the oceanographer Mr. Worthington of the Woods Hole Oceanographic Institution, who joined the ice island party in the fall of 1952.

Every six hours meteorological observations, including measurements of wind, temperature and barometric pressure, have been taken by the personnel manning the meteorological station. There was a rapid rise in the temperature during April, 1952, and from April 30 the temperature was constantly above 0° F., reaching +32° F. the first time on May 15.

By the end of June, the melting was in full swing, the ice was showing through the snow in many places, and there was running water everywhere. The season of most intensive melting began early in July and lasted to the middle of August, when the entire snow cover melted, forming lakes in the troughs between the ridges. These lakes drained off through narrow channels leading from one lake to another, and eventually off the island. In addition, one or two feet of ice melted off the top of the island. Boxes and pieces of equipment which provided insulation were left standing on pedestals of ice, the surrounding ice having melted away.

At this rate of melting, the ice islands floating about in the Polar Sea will eventually dwindle away. It is not likely that they will last more than seventy-five to a hundred years, even if they remain in the Polar Basin.

Various articles and specimens of plant and animal life, which were probably deposited on the island when it was part of the Ellesmere shelf ice, were carried with the streams of melt water and accumulated, together with sand and dirt, at different places on the island. In one place they have found stems, twigs and parts of plants, fish bones, a complete fish about five inches long, and remnants of what appeared to have been a lemming. Three miles from camp they came across a complete set of caribou antlers projecting from the snow, and underneath it they found pieces of skin and fur frozen in the ice.

In April, 1952, tracks of a polar bear were seen on the island not far from the camp. This led us temporarily to believe that animal life might not be so scarce after all in the interior of the Polar Basin. During the entire summer, however, the wild life on or around T-3 consisted of a total of eight single birds, identified as gulls and jaegers. The first one was seen in the middle of June, and the last on August 15. No other wild life was observed. There were no signs of seal or fish in the water, although two specimens of zooplankton (a shrimp and a jellyfish) were collected early in the summer.

These findings, therefore, support the contention that the central North Polar Basin is comparatively lifeless, and offers no possibility for living off the land in the usual sense of the phrase. This means that in order to survive on the ice in the interior of the North Polar Basin rations have to be carried.

However, the possibility still existed that the Polar Sea might contain zooplankton in sufficient quantities to be used as food in case of extreme emergency. This question was explored by the marine biologist, Mr. C. Horvath, representing the USAF Arctic Aeromedical Laboratory, who settled on T-3 in October, 1952, to spend the winter studying the life in the ocean.

He built a shelter of snow blocks covered by canvas, and heated by a Yukon stove, close to the edge of the island, so that he could conveniently collect samples through holes in the pack ice. The shelter was constantly subject to damage by the heavy ice that piled in against the island. Several times huge pressure ridges demolished it and the scientific equipment was pulled away to safety in the nick of time. In the face of these constant troubles he continued lowering his net into the sea, and brought up both zooplankton and plant plankton, zooplankton predominating. He also lowered conical wire traps made of window screens and baited with meat, and caught several thousand marine crustacea (amphipods and isopods). He then lowered lines with hooks through the ice holes, using salmon eggs and beef chunks as bait and left them there overnight. He caught no fish, but the baits were invariably stripped by the crustacea, which appeared to occur in such quantities that they might be important as food for marooned survivors on the polar pack ice.

While the island continued on its course, unaffected by the will of man, powered by the force of wind and weather, it was decided in Washington to continue the project through the coming winter, and by the beginning of June, preparations for the resupply of T-3 for the winter season were in progress. In the middle of June the aircraft loaded with supplies urgently needed to establish a meteorological station for upper air observation moved from Alaska to Thule, ready to proceed as soon as the weather permitted.

On June 15, when the thaw was well under way on T-3, the first sea gull was seen flying over the camp heading south. That day Joe Fletcher's wife gave birth to a daughter. She was named Sila, which is the Eskimo word for weather.

On June 19, T-3 reported that the C-47 had landed in slush ice on the island. It returned the following day with Joe Fletcher, who had then completed three months on his island.

During the fall of 1952 supplies, personnel and equipment were flown in to T-3 in sufficient quantities to allow the group of weather observers and scientists to survive the arctic winter. It was originally planned to land on the frozen lakes during September while there was still daylight, but this proved impossible. It was not until the middle of October that the ice was thick enough to support the landing of C-47's equipped with skis. At this time it was already so dark that runway lights had to be paradropped before the landing could be made. In January, 1953, however, Colonel Streeton of the Alaskan Air Command made two landings with a C-54 on wheels without any trouble.

While the ice island jerked and twisted through the long winter night, battered from all sides by the pack ice during storms and blinding blizzards, the crew of specialists proceeded with the collection of their valuable data in comfort and peace. In March, 1953, as T-3 was gradually approaching Greenland, the project was transferred entirely to the Northeast Air Command, while the technical direction of the research activity remained with Dr. Crary, at the Cambridge Research Center.

Judging by the present trend of its movements, T-3 is now on its way back to its starting point at Ellesmere Island. From there it will probably begin a new circle through the Polar Sea which it will take several years to complete. Providing it escapes the East Greenland Current it may form the basis for a floating scientific laboratory throughout the next generation. Similar bases may be established on the other known ice islands, and on those which in the future will break off from the shelf ice off Ellesmere Island.

The group of ice islands on T-3 now numbers about ten—

a station commander, a cook, a couple of radio men and meteorologists, two geophysicists, a marine biologist and an oceanographer. It is planned to add a glaciologist to the party in the near future.

The T-3 experiment has already yielded important scientific contributions to our knowledge of the remotest part of the North Polar regions in the fields of meteorology, oceanography, geophysics, glaciology, and biology. Some of our previous knowledge has been confirmed, and new important facts have been discovered.

Of the greatest immediate importance are the meteorological observations which have poured in regularly from T-3 ever since April, 1952, and which are filling in a wide gap in the data vitally needed for more accurate weather forecasts. In addition to routine observations at ground level, balloons with weather instruments are sent up twice a day. This study of arctic meteorology will eventually throw light on the atmospheric circulation in the Northern Hemisphere and on the origin and cause of cyclones. The present study of ice formation and currents, and their relation to possible climatic changes, will probably turn out to have a bearing on the weather on the North American continent and in Europe—a fact pointed out by Nansen half a century ago. The data so far collected have produced further evidence of the warming up of the arctic regions, and of the glacial recession which has taken place during the last few decades.

The T-3 experiment has convinced us that the polar pack ice in the central North Polar Basin represents the most inhospitable environmental condition of the North Polar regions: a barren desolate waste of polar ice where we encountered killing cold and numbing winds and where man can survive only when supplied with the best of equipment. Our experiences there have shown the need for improved shelters and clothing for successful survival in these areas. As I have said, living "off the land" is out of the question, unless the studies now in progress reveal that the zooplankton are sufficiently plentiful to be used as food. Survival rations, therefore, have to be carried, a fact that necessitates the development of a concentrated ration yielding the maximum nutritional value per unit of weight. In addition, small efficient cookers or stoves may have to be constructed as a source of heat for individual survival on the polar pack ice. Furthermore, the T-3 experience has made it clear that in order to combat successfully the unique conditions of the "wet cold" during the summer in the pack ice, a new type of equipment and clothing needs to be worked out, entirely different from those intended for survival in the dry cold. Finally, the experiences gained from T-3 have supported our previous views that survival on the pack ice does not require superhuman qualities or efforts. Know-how, practical experience, suitable shelters, adequate clothing and sufficient food are all that are needed. *HAM GEAR TOO!*

The extensive air operations involved in the T-3 project have served to create confidence in the use of aircraft as a means of transportation in the central North Polar Basin, and in the reliability of polar navigation. The establishment of a base on T-3 has brought military operations into the heart of the North Polar Basin and has created an entirely new factor in the military control of these regions, for the base may provide data for weather predictions essential to military air operations along the entire arctic route of defense. This or similar bases may even serve as staging bases for refueling and fighter coverage. The radio beacon on T-3 means safer navigation across the top of the world. The station on this floating berg may serve as a base for Air Search and Rescue operations when aircraft are downed in the North

Polar regions. Finally, if need be, T-3 and similar bases may form part of the radar network watching the roof entrance to the North American continent.

Of even greater importance than the military aspects is the fact that the T-3 project has made practical use of the North Pole area as a highway in aerial communications, linking the continents through the sky.

Although the work has barely started, the ice island project is already beginning to pay off. "Project Icicle" has pioneered a new approach to polar exploration. It is the beginning of a large-scale scientific exploration of the last remaining blank spot on the polar map.

Bibliography

AASGAARD, GUNNAR. "Store Norske Spitsbergen Kulkompani A/S." *Tidsskr. for kjemi, bergvesen og metallurgi*, 10. No. 2b. Oslo, 1950. Pp. 122-26.

AHLMANN, H. W:SON. "The Present Climatic Fluctuation." *Geogr. journ.*, CXII. London, 1949. Pp. 165-95.

———. "Glacier Variations and Climatic Fluctuations." *Bowman Memorial Lectures*, No. 3. *Amer. Geogr. Soc.*, New York, 1953.

Andrée's Story. The Complete Record of His Polar Flight, 1897. From the diaries and journals of S. A. Andrée, Nils Strindberg, and K. Fraenkel, found on White Island in the summer of 1930 and edited by the Swedish Society for Anthropology and Geography. The Viking Press, New York, 1930.

BREITFUSS, L. "Neue wertvolle Beiträge zur Erschliessung der Innerarktis." *Peterm. geogr. Mitt.*, 93. Gotha, 1949. Pp. 33-35.

CONNELL, FRANK H. "Trichinosis in the Arctic: a Review." *Arctic*, 2. Montreal and New York, 1949. Pp. 98-107.

CRARY, A. P., COTELL, R. D., and SEXTON, T. F. "Preliminary report on Scientific Work on 'Fletcher's Ice Island,' T3." *Arctic*, 5. Montreal and New York, 1952. Pp. 211-23.

DEGE, WILHELM. "Das Nordostland von Spitsbergen. Studien zu einer Landeskunde." *Polarforschung*, II. Kiel, 1946-47. Pp. 72-83, 154-63.

DUFRESNE, FRANK. *Alaska's animals and fishes.* A. S. Barnes, New York, 1946.

EKMAN, V. WALFRID. "Om jordrotationens inverkan på vindströmmar i hafvet." *Nyt Mag. for Naturvidensk*, 40. Oslo, 1902. Pp. 37-63.

ELBO, J. G. "Cryolite and the Mine at Ivigtut, West Greenland." *Polar Record*, 5. Cambridge, 1948. Pp. 185-88.

FLETCHER, JOSEPH O. "Three Months on an Arctic Ice Island." *Nat. Geogr. Mag.*, CIII. Washington, 1953. Pp. 489-504.

ILLINGWORTH, FRANK. *North of the Circle.* W. Hodge and Co., London, 1951.

JACOBSEN, N. KINGO. "Arktiske problemstillinger i relation til besejlingen." *Geogr. Tidsskr.*, 51. Copenhagen, 1951. Pp. 94-133.

——, with SVEISTRUP, P. P. *Erhverv og kultur langs polarkredsen.* Ed. by Det Grønlandske Selskab. Copenhagen, 1950.

KOCH, LAUGE. "The East Greenland Ice." C. A. Reitzel, Copenhagen, 1945. *Medd. om Grønland,* 130. No. 3.

KOENIG, L. S., GREENAWAY, K. R., DUNBAR, MOIRA, and HATTERSLEY-SMITH, G. "Arctic Ice-Islands." *Arctic,* 5. Montreal and New York, 1952. Pp. 67-103.

KOETTLITZ, REGINALD. "Contribution to the Natural History of the Polar Bear." *Proc. R. Phys. Soc. of Edinburgh,* XIV. Edinburgh, 1902. Pp. 266-77.

LEFFINGWELL, ERNEST DE K. *The Canning River Region, Northern Alaska.* Washington, 1919. U. S. Geol. Survey, Prof. paper, No. 109.

MONTGOMERY, MARGARET R. "Further Notes on Ice Islands in the Canadian Arctic." *Arctic,* 5. Montreal and New York, 1952. Pp. 183-87.

NANSEN, FRIDTJOF. *Farthest North: Being the Record of a Voyage of Exploration of the Ship Fram 1893-1896* . . . Vols. 1 and 2. Harper, New York, 1897.

——. *The Oceanography of the North Polar Basin.* Oslo. 1902. *The Norwegian North Polar Expedition 1893-1896.* Scientific Results. No. 9 (Vol. 3).

PAPANIN, IVAN. *Life on an Icefloe.* Hutchinson, London, 1939, 1944.

PEARY, ROBERT E. *Nearest the Pole*: A Narrative of the Polar Expedition of the Peary Arctic Club in the S.S. "Roosevelt" 1905-1906. Doubleday, New York, 1907.

——. *The North Pole,* Its Discovery in 1909 under the Auspices of the Peary Arctic Club. Stokes, New York, 1910.

PEDERSEN, ALWIN. *Der Eisbär. Verbreitung und Lebensweise.* E. Bruun & Co., Copenhagen, 1945.

RENDAHL, HJ., and PEDERSEN, ALWIN. *Arktiska faaglar.* Ahlen & Söners förlag, Stockholm, 1938.

RODAHL, KAARE. "Content of Vitamin C in Arctic Plants." *Trans. Bot. Soc. Edinb.,* XXXIV, P. I. Edinburgh, 1944. Pp. 205-10.

RODAHL, KAARE. "Vitamin B$_1$ Content of Arctic Plants and Animal Tissue." *Trans. Bot. Soc. Edinb.*, XXXIV, P. II. Edinburgh, 1945. Pp. 244-51.

——. *The Ice-Capped Island: Greenland.* Blackie & Son, London, 1946.

——. *Nytt land under vingene.* Gyldendal, Oslo, 1948.

——. "Vitamin Sources in Arctic Regions." A. W. Brøggers Boktrykkeri. Oslo, 1949. *Skrifter.* Norsk. Polarinstitutt. No. 91.

——. "The Toxic Effect of Polar Bear Liver." A. W. Bröggers Boktrykkeri. Oslo, 1949. *Skrifter.* Norsk Polarinstitutt. No. 92.

——. "Basal Metabolism of the Eskimo." *Journ. Nutrition,* 48, No. 3. Philadelphia, 1952. Pp. 359-68.

——. " 'Spekk-finger' or Sealer's Finger." *Arctic,* 5. Montreal and New York, 1952. Pp. 235-40.

——, and MOORE, T. "The Vitamin A Content and Toxicity of Bear and Seal Liver." *Biochem. journ.,* 37. London, 1943. Pp. 166-68.

SEIDENFADEN, GUNNAR. *Moderne arktisk Forskning.* Jespersen og Pio, Copenhagen, 1938.

STEFANSSON, VILHJALMUR. *The Friendly Arctic.* Macmillan, New York, 1945.

——. "The Question of Living by Forage in the Arctic." *Arktis,* 2. Gotha, 1929. Pp. 11-15.

STEFANSSON, VILHJALMUR (editor). "The Three Voyages of Martin Frobisher in Search of a Passage to Cathay and India by the North West, A.D. 1576-78. Vol. I, II. The Argonaut Press, London, 1938.

SVERDRUP, HARALD U. "Aufgaben, Bemannung und Ausrüstung einer wissenschaftlichen Beobachtungsstation auf dem Treibeis bei 1-2 jähriger Überwinterung in der inneren Arktis." *Arktis,* 1. Gotha, 1928. Pp. 29-36.

——. "Drift-ice and Ice-drift." (Scient. res. of the Andrée-exp. 1.) *Geografiska Annaler,* 13. Stockholm, 1931. Pp. 121-40.

——. "Dyrelivet i drivisen. Efter erfaringene på 'Maud'—ferden." *Naturen,* 54. Bergen, 1930. Pp. 133-45.

——. "Physical Oceanography of the North Polar Sea." *Arctic,* 3. Montreal and New York, 1950. Pp. 178-86.

——. "Übersicht über das Klima des Polarmeeres und des Kanadischen Archipels." *Handbuch der Klimatologie.* Berlin, 1935. Bd. II. Teil K.

THOMSEN, H. (Prepared by). "The State of the Ice in the Arctic Seas 1949." (Appendix to the Nautical-Meteorological Annual 1949). G. E. C. Gad., Copenhagen, 1951.

ZUKRIEGEL, JOSEF. "Cryologia Maris." *Travaux geographiques Tchèques,* 15. Prague, 1935.

INDEX

233

Set in Linotype Caledonia
Format by Robert Cheney
Manufactured by The Haddon Craftsmen, Inc.
Published by HARPER & BROTHERS, *New York*

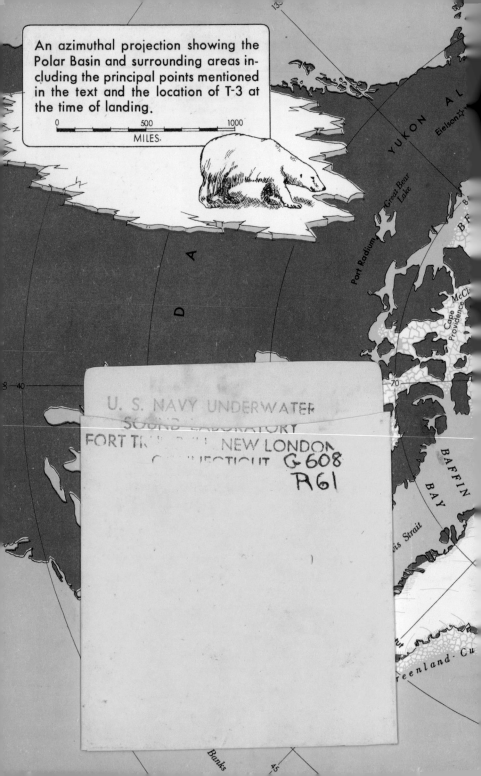

An azimuthal projection showing the Polar Basin and surrounding areas including the principal points mentioned in the text and the location of T-3 at the time of landing.

0   500   1000
MILES.